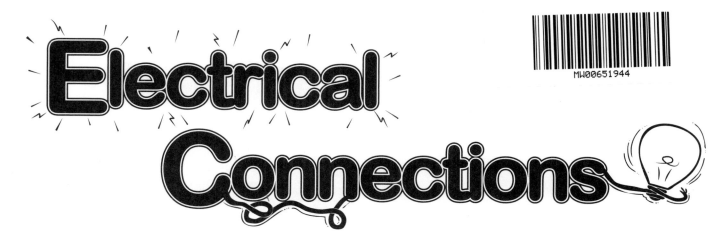

Electrical Connections

Developed and Published
by

AIMS Education Foundation

This book contains materials developed by the AIMS Education Foundation. **AIMS** (**A**ctivities **I**ntegrating **M**athematics and **S**cience) began in 1981 with a grant from the National Science Foundation. The non-profit AIMS Education Foundation publishes hands-on instructional materials that build conceptual understanding. The foundation also sponsors a national program of professional development through which educators may gain expertise in teaching math and science.

Copyright © 2011 by the AIMS Education Foundation

All rights reserved. No part of this book or associated digital media may be reproduced or transmitted in any form or by any means—including photocopying, taping, or information storage/retrieval systems—except as noted below.

• A person or school purchasing this AIMS publication is hereby granted permission to make up to 200 copies of any portion of it (or the files on the accompanying disc), provided these copies will be used for educational purposes and only at one school site.

• For a workshop or conference session, presenters may make one copy of any portion of a purchased activity for each participant, with a limit of five activities or up to one-third of a book, whichever is less.

• All copies must bear the AIMS Education Foundation copyright information.

• Modifications to AIMS pages (e.g., separating page elements for use on an interactive white board) are permitted only within the classroom or school for which they were purchased, or by presenters at conferences or workshops. Interactive white board files may not be uploaded to any third-party website or otherwise distributed. AIMS artwork and content may not be used on non-AIMS materials.

AIMS users may purchase unlimited duplication rights for making more than 200 copies, for use at more than one school site, or for use on the Internet. Contact us or visit the AIMS website for complete details.

AIMS Education Foundation
P.O. Box 8120, Fresno, CA 93747-8120 • 888.733.2467 • aimsedu.org

ISBN 978-1-60519-044-0

Printed in the United States of America

I Hear and I Forget,

I See and I Remember,

I Do and I Understand.
-Chinese Proverb

 © 2011 AIMS Education Foundation

Electrical Connections

Table of Contents

© 2011 AIMS Education Foundation

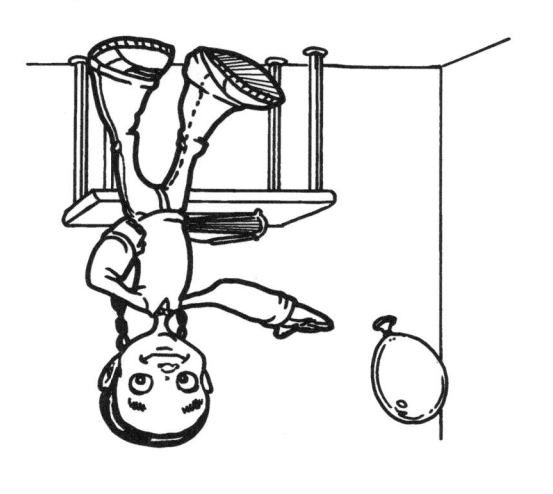

When the negatively charged balloon is brought near a wall, it **induces** a positive charge near the surface of the wall. (The extra electrons on the balloon repel electrons near the surface of the wall.) Since opposite charges attract, the balloon sticks to the wall.

STATIC ELECTRICITY

Have you ever rubbed a balloon on your hair and then stuck it to the wall? Static electricity was at work!

All matter is made up of tiny particles called atoms. Most atoms contain three basic parts.

- **Protons** have a positive electrical charge (+).

- **Electrons** have a negative electrical charge (–).

- **Neutrons** have no electrical charge.

When a balloon is rubbed on your hair, it gains electrons from your hair. It becomes negatively charged. Your hair becomes positively charged. It will stick up because it is attracted to the negatively charged balloon. Unlike charges attract each other.

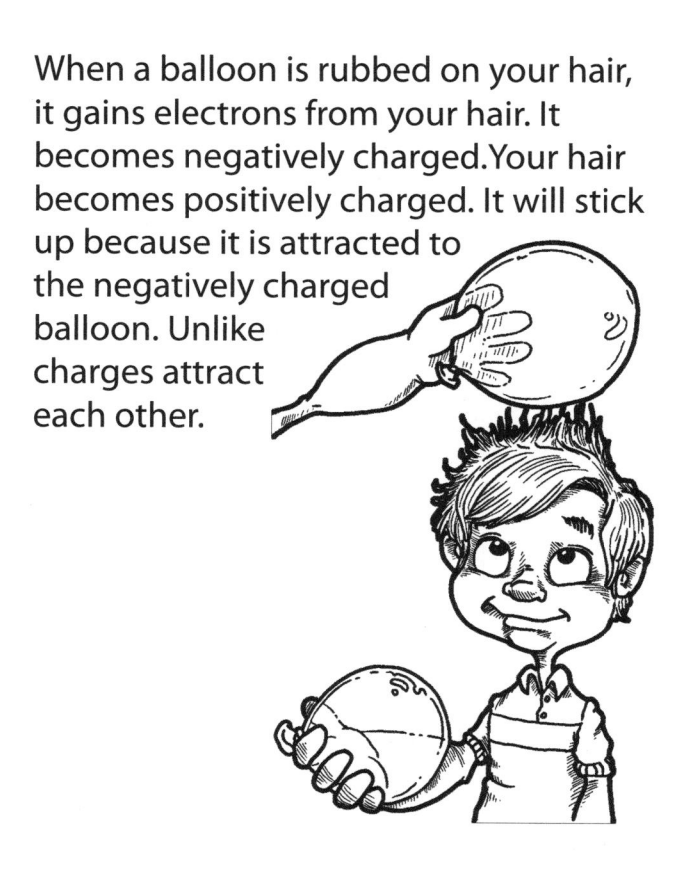

Sometimes objects gain or lose electrons through **friction** (rubbing two things together). When this happens, the objects become electrically charged.

If an object gains electrons when it is rubbed, it becomes negatively charged. It has more electrons (–) than protons (+). If an object loses electrons when it is rubbed, it becomes positively charged. It has more protons (+) than electrons (–).

Most objects, such as balloons, normally have about the same number of electrons and protons. This makes them electrically balanced.

A basic rule of electric charges is that like charges repel and unlike charges attract.

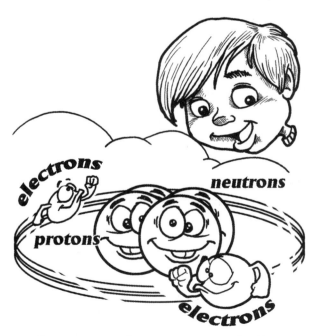

Protons and neutrons are in the **nucleus** or central core of an atom. The electrons orbit around the nucleus.

ELECTRICAL CONNECTIONS

© 2011 AIMS Education Foundation

Static Strokes

Topic
Static electricity

Key Question
How does a statically-charged object affect other objects?

Learning Goals
Students will:
• explore static electricity, and
• observe the effects of positive and negative charges as they attract and repel.

Guiding Documents
Project 2061 Benchmarks
• *Without touching them, material that has been electrically charged pulls on all other materials and may either push or pull other charged materials.*
• *Keep records of their investigations and observations.*

NRC Standard
• *Plan and conduct a simple investigation.*

Science
Physical science
     static electricity

Integrated Processes
Observing
Comparing and contrasting
Predicting
Generalizing

Materials
Plastic wrap (see *Management 3*)
Paper towels
Small objects: paper clips, salt, small bits of aluminum foil, Styrofoam pieces, thread (see *Management 6*)
Students pages

Background Information
All objects are composed of atoms that contain positive (produced by protons) and negative (produced by electrons) electric charges. Most objects have no net electric charge and are electrically balanced because they have approximately the same

numbers of electrons as protons. Static electricity occurs when objects become unbalanced electrically. Some materials easily lose or gain electrons, causing them to have, respectively, a net positive or negative charge. When certain materials are rubbed together (e.g., your shoes on a carpet or the plastic wrap and paper towels in this activity), friction causes electrons to be transferred from one material to the other, producing the unbalanced charges we experience as static electricity.

A key property of electricity is that like charges repel each other, while opposite charges attract. Statically charged objects can produce static charges in other objects. For example, a negatively charged balloon sticks to a wall because its negative charge repels electrons in the atoms at the wall's surface (causing the atoms to become polarized), thus inducing a positive charge. Static electricity is most easily observed on cool, dry days when conditions keep the charges from dispersing easily.

Management
1. Have students work in groups of three or four.
2. This activity works best on cool, dry days or inside air-conditioned classrooms.
3. Not all plastic wraps are equal in their static ability. Test any wrap you buy to see that it works.
4. If you don't want to use plastic wrap for *Part Two*, inflated balloons work well. Charge them by rubbing them on clothes or hair.
5. Make sure that the desktops are free of soaps or other cleaners.
6. Various small objects can be placed in small zipper-type plastic bags for ease of distribution.

Procedure
Part One
1. Distribute a piece of plastic wrap and a paper towel to each student.
2. Demonstrate for students how to charge the plastic wrap by placing it flat on a desk and vigorously rubbing it with a paper towel.
3. Tell them to lift the plastic wrap from the desk by one corner and observe what happens. [The plastic wrap will initially cling to the desk and when lifted will cling to hands or other nearby objects.] Direct them to record their observations.

7   © 2011 AIMS Education Foundation

4. Have students charge the plastic wrap again and pick it up by the midpoints of two opposite sides (see illustration.) Ask them to observe what happens and record their observations. [The plastic wrap will make a tent shape since the opposite sides have the same charge and repel each other.]

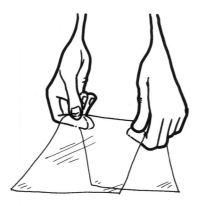

5. Discuss what happened in each case.
6. Make certain that students understand that static electricity is responsible for the phenomena they observed. Help students to understand that this electricity does not flow through circuits; it is static, which means it doesn't move.

Part Two
1. Distribute objects to be tested.
2. Discuss the *Key Question:* How does a statically-charged object affect other objects?
3. Tell students to work with one set of objects at a time. Invite them to predict what will happen when the charged plastic wrap is held above the objects. After recording their predictions for the first object, the paper clips, have students charge their plastic wrap and, in pairs, lift the plastic wrap by the four corners and slowly lower it until it is six to 10 centimeters above the objects. Ask them to observe what happens and record their observations.
4. Allow students time to predict and test the next four objects. Remind them to record their observations.
5. Invite students to choose four or five objects that they would like to test. Have them fill in the chart with the objects' names and their predictions as to what might happen. Some suggested objects are pencil shavings, erasers, eraser rubbings, iron filings, bits of tissue, and plastic chips.
6. Discuss the results and have students fill in the summary statement at the bottom of the page.

Connecting Learning
1. Why did the plastic wrap cling to your arm when you picked it up? [My arm and the plastic wrap had unlike charges that caused the attraction.]
2. Why did the plastic wrap make a tent shape when held by the midpoints of opposite sides? [The two sides of the plastic wrap had like charges that caused them to repel each other.]
3. Why did the charged plastic wrap pick up some objects but not others? [The attractive force caused by the static electricity was enough to overcome the force of gravity for the lighter objects, but not the heavier ones.]
4. What are you wondering now?

Extensions
1. Have students move their fingers close above the surface of the charged plastic wrap as it is attracting bits of Styrofoam or other objects. They will be fascinated by the results.
2. Challenge the students to see if they can make some of the objects "dance." This is easy to do with Styrofoam bits or short lengths of thread.
3. Repeat *Part Two* using balloons instead of plastic wrap.
4. Make "magic wands" by rubbing plastic straws or pens with a paper towel. They will attract light objects. Note: not all types of plastic work well for this.
5. Read about Benjamin Franklin and his experiments with static electricity.

Static Strokes

Key Question

How does a statically-charged object affect other objects?

Learning Goals

Students will:

- explore static electricity, and
- observe the effects of positive and negative charges as they attract and repel.

 © 2011 AIMS Education Foundation

Static Strokes
Part One

Place a piece of plastic wrap flat on your desk and rub it with a paper towel. Pick the plastic wrap up by one corner.

What happens?

Place the plastic wrap on your desk and rub it with a paper towel again. Pick the plastic wrap up by the midpoints of two opposite sides.

What happens?

Static Strokes

Part Two

How does a statically-charged object affect other objects?

Charge the plastic wrap. Predict what will happen when it is held six to 10 centimeters above the following objects. Record your predictions. Hold the plastic wrap flat above the objects listed. Record your observations.

Objects	Predictions	Observations
paper clips		
Styrofoam		
small pieces of aluminum foil		
cotton thread		
salt		

© 2011 AIMS Education Foundation

Static Strokes

Connecting Learning

1. Why did the plastic wrap cling to your arm when you picked it up?

2. Why did the plastic wrap make a tent shape when held by the midpoints of opposite sides?

3. Why did the charged plastic wrap pick up some objects but not others?

4. What are you wondering now?

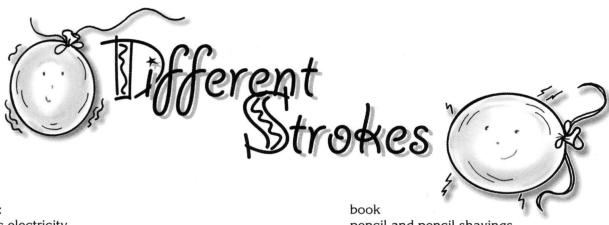

Different Strokes

Topic
Static electricity

Key Questions
1. How does a statically-charged object affect other objects?
2. How do balloons with like and unlike charges interact with each other and with other materials?

Learning Goal
Students will experiment with static electricity and discover some of its properties.

Guiding Documents
Project 2061 Benchmark
- *Without touching them, material that has been electrically charged pulls on all other materials and may either push or pull on other charged materials.*

NRC Standard
- *Use data to construct a reasonable explanation.*

Math
Measurement
   length

Science
Physical science
   static electricity

Integrated Processes
Observing
Classifying
Identifying and controlling variables
Recording data
Drawing conclusions

Materials
For each group:
   two balloons
   piece of nylon material or paper towel
   two 30-cm pieces of thread
   small bits of paper
   book
   pencil and pencil shavings
   piece of plastic wrap
   plastic ruler
   tape

For each student:
   student pages

Background Information
Some materials develop static charges when they are rubbed together. This happens because there is a transfer of electrons (negative charges) from one material to another. The material that gains electrons becomes negatively charged, while the material that loses electrons becomes positively charged. For example, a rubber balloon rubbed by a piece of nylon picks up electrons and becomes negatively charged while the nylon loses electrons and becomes positively charged.

When any two substances listed below are rubbed together, the substance *higher* on the list (which is called the *triboelectric* or *electrostatic* series) will become positively charged, while the *lower* one will become negatively charged. The farther apart the two substances are on the list, the greater the charge produced. In each case, the material higher on the list *gives up* electrons, (negative charges) to become positively charged, while the other material *receives* extra electrons and becomes negatively charged.

Positive Charge (gives up electrons)
   glass
   nylon
   wool
   silk
   paper
   wood
   sealing wax
   Styrofoam
   rubber
   plastic wrap
Negative Charge (gains electrons)

If two balloons are rubbed with the same material, they will both have the same charge. Since like charges repel, the balloons will repel each other and not touch. If certain objects are placed between two similarly charged balloons, an opposite charge is induced in the objects and both balloons are attracted to the object. Other objects do not become charged by induction when placed between two similarly charged balloons and the balloons continue to repel each other.

When two balloons are rubbed with different materials, the type and strength of their charges will differ, depending on factors such as their position in the triboelectric series. For example, when one balloon is rubbed with nylon and another is rubbed with plastic wrap, they will have opposite charges and will attract each other. This happens because opposite charges attract.

Management
1. Static electricity lessons are best done on cool, dry days. Warm, moist air will conduct electric charges away from an object as soon as they are formed. An invisible coat of moisture on materials permits the electric charges to run off into the area surrounding the object.
2. Gather all materials for the activity and place them in a basket or box for each group.
3. Students can use their own hair to charge the balloons instead of nylon or paper towels. Their hair should be clean and dry.
4. Not all plastic wraps are equal in their static ability. Test any wrap you buy to see that it works.

Procedure
Part One
1. Ask the first *Key Question:* "How does a statically charged object affect other objects?"
2. Rub a balloon with a piece of nylon or paper towel and touch the balloon to a wall. Discuss what happens and why. [It has become negatively charged and induces a positive charge near the surface of the wall. Since opposite charges attract, it sticks to the wall because of the electrostatic forces.]
3. Tell students that they will be observing the effects that a charged balloon has on different objects. Distribute the first student page and have students do the tasks as they are presented.
4. Discuss the results as a class. Have students write their conclusions in the space provided at the bottom of the page.

Part Two
1. Ask the second *Key Question:* "How do balloons with like and unlike charges interact with each other and with other materials?"
2. Have students blow up their second balloons and tie each balloon to a 30-cm piece of thread.
3. Tell students to tape the balloons to the edge of a table so that there is a three to five centimeter space between the balloons.
4. Direct students to charge one balloon by rubbing it with a piece of plastic wrap (giving it a positive charge) and the other by rubbing it with a piece of nylon (giving it a negative charge). Have students observe the effects of the unlike charges and record what happens on the second student page.
5. Have students charge both balloons with a piece of nylon, giving them both a negative charge. Tell them to observe the effects of like charges on the two balloons and record what happens.
6. Have students charge both balloons by rubbing them with a piece of nylon and then hold their hands, plastic rulers, paper, and plastic wrap between the two balloons. Tell them to observe and record what happens. Encourage students to try other materials and observe the results.
7. Discuss the results as a class, and have students write their conclusions in the space provided at the bottom of the page.

Connecting Learning
1. What were the results of one of the activities? Explain why you think it happened the way it did.
2. Do you think the results would be different if it were a rainy day? Explain.
3. What happens when a statically-charged balloon is brought near light objects?
4. What happens when a statically-charged balloon is brought near heavy objects?
5. How do the two balloons interact when they have opposite charges? [They attract each other.]
6. How do the two balloons interact when they have the same charge? [They repel each other.]
7. What happens when an object is placed between balloons with like charges? Does the type of object make a difference?
8. What are you wondering now?

Extensions
1. Use Styrofoam cups instead of balloons and test the results.
2. Repeat *Part Two* using positively charged balloons.
3. Ask students to conduct their own static electricity experiments and share the results with the class.

Key Questions

1. How does a statically-charged object affect other objects?

2. How do balloons with like and unlike charges interact with each other and with other materials?

Learning Goal

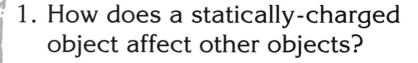

experiment with static electricity and discover some of its properties.

Different Strokes

Part One

How does a statically-charged balloon affect other objects?

Blow up a balloon and knot the end. Charge the balloon by rubbing it with a piece of nylon. Complete each test below and mark the statement that describes the result.

Bring a charged balloon near small pieces of paper. Observe what happens.	affects paper	no effect on paper
Bring a charged balloon near a piece of thread. Observe what happens.	affects thread	no effect on thread
Bring a charged balloon near a pencil. Observe what happens.	affects pencil	no effect on pencil
Bring a charged balloon near somebody's hair. Observe what happens.	affects hair	no effect on hair
Bring a charged balloon near a book. Observe what happens.	affects books	no effect on books
Bring a charged balloon near some pencil shavings. Observe what happens.	affects shavings	no effect on shavings

Conclusions:

Blow up a second balloon. Use two pieces of thread and tape to hang both balloons from the edge of a table so they are 3-5 cm apart.

Charge one balloon with a piece of plastic wrap and the other with nylon. Observe the interaction.	opposite charges attract	opposite charges repel	no effect
Charge both balloons by rubbing with a piece of nylon. Observe the interaction.	like charges attract	like charges repel	no effect
Charge both balloons by rubbing with a piece of nylon. Hold your hand between the balloons. Does the interaction between the balloons change?		interaction affected by hand	interaction not affected
Charge both balloons with nylon. Hold a plastic ruler between them. Does the interaction between the balloons change?		interaction affected by ruler	interaction not affected
Charge both balloons with nylon. Hold a piece of paper between them. Does the interaction between the balloons change?		interaction affected by paper	interaction not affected
Charge both balloons with nylon. Hold a piece of plastic wrap between them. Does the interaction between the balloons change?		interaction affected by wrap	interaction not affected

Conclusions:

17 © 2011 AIMS Education Foundation

Connecting Learning

1. What were the results of one of the activities? Explain why you think it happened the way it did.

2. Do you think the results would be different if it were a rainy day?

3. What happens when a statically-charged balloon is brought near light objects?

4. What happens when a statically-charged balloon is brought near heavy objects?

5. How do the two balloons interact when they have opposite charges?

18 © 2011 AIMS Education Foundation

Connecting Learning

6. How do the two balloons interact when they have the same charge?

7. What happens when an object is placed between the balloons with like charges? Does the type of object make a difference?

8. What are you wondering now?

Static Sensations

Topic
Static electricity

Key Question
How can you use your senses to experience the static electric force?

Learning Goal
Students will explore and experience the static electric force using their senses of feeling, hearing, and seeing.

Guiding Document
Project 2061 Benchmark
- *Without touching them, material that has been electrically charged pulls on all other materials and may either push or pull other charged materials.*

Science
Physical science
   static electricity

Integrated Processes
Observing
Comparing and contrasting
Collecting and recording data

Materials
Rubber balloons, one per student
Paper clips, one per student
Fluorescent bulb (see *Management 6*)
Student pages

Background Information
   Static electricity is a normal part of our everyday world, yet we rarely think of it as a force. In fact, static electricity is one manifestation of a fundamental force in the universe—the electromagnetic force. Some of the key properties of this fundamental force, in its static electricity form, can be easily observed by elementary school students using their senses of feeling, hearing, and seeing.

   One of the key characteristics of the static electric force is that it is able to act at a distance and make things move without coming in direct contact with them. In addition, this force both attracts and repels, depending, respectively, on whether unlike or like charges are involved. In these two important ways, this force is very different from the normal pushing and pulling forces we encounter in our everyday experience.

Management
1. This activity has three main parts and an optional fourth part. All four parts can be completed in one class period. Each part can be done with the whole class or in small groups. In either case, students need their own balloons so that they can experience the static electric force firsthand.
2. This activity works best in cool, dry conditions.
3. Balloons should be inflated ahead of time. Balloons that are inflated close to their maximum size produce a better static charge than under-inflated balloons.
4. Balloons can be charged by rubbing them on students' hair or clothing. Not all materials will charge the balloons equally, however. For example, clothing containing nylon or wool will work better than cotton clothing.
5. The fourth part of this activity is optional. If you choose to do it, you will need to get a fluorescent bulb and let students take turns lighting it with their charged balloons. The darker the room, the easier it is to see the faint light produced when the bulb is lit by the static discharge.
6. Any kind of fluorescent lightbulb will work, but the tube bulbs like those in most classrooms work best.

Procedure
Part One
1. Distribute the balloons and the first student page.
2. Ask the question: *"How can you use your sense of feeling to experience the static electric force?"*
3. Demonstrate how to charge the inflated balloon by stroking it on your hair or clothing.
4. Have students follow the directions on the student page. After they do each part, lead them in a discussion and have them record their answers.

Part Two
1. Give students the second student page.
2. Ask the question: *How can you use your sense of hearing to experience the static electric force?*
3. Have students follow the directions on the second student page. After they do each part, lead them in a discussion and have them record their answers.

Part Three
1. Distribute the third student page.
2. Ask the question: *How can you use your sense of seeing to experience the static electric force?*
3. Have students follow the directions on the student page. After they do each part, lead them in a discussion and have them record their answers.

4. Conclude the activity with a whole-class discussion that focuses on how students used their various senses to observe the static electric force in various ways. If appropriate, discuss the static electric force in greater detail.

Part Four
1. Give students the fourth student page.
2. Ask the question: *What happens when you bring your charged balloon near the electrodes of a fluorescent light bulb?*
3. Put out a fluorescent bulb and turn off the classroom lights. Let students take turns lighting the bulb by charging their balloons and then letting them discharge on the bulb electrodes. Multiple discharges are possible by rotating different parts of the balloon near the electrodes.

Connecting Learning
Part One
1. What did you notice when you moved the charged balloon just above the back of your hand? [Students should feel a tingling as the static charge attracts the hairs on the backs of their hands.]
2. What did you notice when you moved the charged balloon just above the palm of your hand? [Students will not likely feel any sensation since there are no hairs on the palms of their hands.]
3. What did you notice when you moved the balloon around your head? [Students will notice the charge in some areas more than others.]

Part Two
1. What did you hear when you brought a paper clip near your charged balloon? [Depending on the amount of charge, students will hear either faint or strong crackles as the static charge jumps to the paper clip.]
2. What did you hear when you brought other objects close to your charged balloon? [Depending on material, students will either hear crackling or not hear anything. The crackling only occurs when the static charge jumps across an air gap, and this will only happen with certain materials—the better conducting the material, the more likely it is to hear the crackle.]
3. What can you tell about the static electric force from this experience? [Static electricity can be observed by hearing it. The static electricity makes a crackling sound as it jumps across to the paper clip. The crackling sound can be heard with some materials, but not others.]

Part Three
1. What did you see when you lowered your charged balloon over your paper? [The paper was attracted and was pulled up to the balloon.]
2. What did you notice when you brought the balloon near various other materials? [The charged balloon will cause most light objects to move and attach themselves to the balloon. Although the charged balloon also attracts heavier objects, the static electric force isn't able to overcome the gravitational force and pick them up.]
3. What happened when you held your charged balloon next to the wall and let go? [The balloon stuck to the wall.]

Part Four
1. What did you see when you brought your charged balloon near the electrodes of the fluorescent bulb? [The static electricity discharged and lit the bulb.]
2. What did you notice when you brought various parts of the balloon near the electrodes? [There were multiple discharges that lit up the bulb.]
3. Forces often move things. In this activity, what moved? [The electric charge in the form of electrons that jumped from the balloon to the electrodes.]
4. Lightning is a powerful example of static electricity in nature. How is this experiment like lightning and how is it different? [Alike: Both are discharges of static electricity. In both cases, electric charges move rapidly from one area to another. Both produce sound and light. Different: Lightning is much more dangerous and powerful. The thunder caused by lightning is much greater than the crackle created as the balloon discharges. Lightning can be observed with the sense of smell since it ionizes the air and this creates a distinctive odor.]
5. What have you learned about the static electric force from all four parts of this activity? [The static electric force acts at a distance. The static force attracts various small objects. The static charge can be observed using the senses of feeling, hearing, and seeing.]
6. What are you wondering now?

Extensions
1. Have students experiment with other ways to charge the balloons.
2. Have students charge other materials, like plastic wrap, and see if they can notice a difference between these materials and the balloon.
3. In the examples used in this activity, the static force always attracts. Have students try to create a situation in which the static force repels.
4. Lightning is nature's static electric light and sound show. Students can research lightning and write a report on it.

Static Sensations

Key Question

How can you use your senses to experience the static electric force?

Learning Goal

Students will:

explore and experience the static electric force using their senses of feeling, hearing, and seeing.

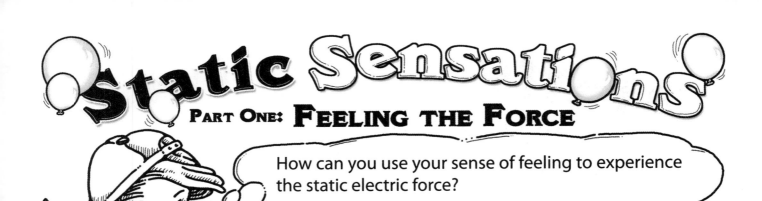

Static Sensations

PART ONE: FEELING THE FORCE

How can you use your sense of feeling to experience the static electric force?

Charge your balloon by stroking it on your hair or clothing. Hold the balloon above the back of your hand without letting it touch. Move the balloon back and forth. Can you feel the static electric force? Try to describe what you feel.

Charge the balloon again and move it just above the palm of your hand without letting it touch. What do you notice this time?

Charge the balloon once more and try to feel the static charge by holding the balloon near various parts of your face and head. Describe what you discover.

In this first part of the activity, you have used your sense of feeling to experience the static electric force. This force is able to act at a distance without making direct contact with an object. How did this experiment demonstrate this?

What else can you say about the static force from this experience?

24   © 2011 AIMS Education Foundation

Static Sensations

PART TWO: HEARING THE FORCE

How can you use your sense of hearing to experience the static electric force?

Charge your balloon and hold it in one hand. With your other hand, slowly bring a paper clip close to the charged part of the balloon (the part that was rubbed). Move the paper clip back and forth over the charged surface of the balloon without letting it touch. What do you hear when you do this?

Charge the balloon again and slowly bring other objects close to the balloon. What do you hear?

In this second part, you have used your sense of hearing to experience the static electric force. What can you tell about the static electric force from this experience?

 © 2011 AIMS Education Foundation

Static Sensations

Part Three: Seeing the Force

How can you use your sense of seeing to experience the static electric force?

Charge your balloon. Slowly lower your balloon over this page. What do you see when you do this?

Charge the balloon again and slowly bring it near a variety of other objects. What do you see?

Charge the balloon once more and let it touch the wall. Let go of the balloon. What do you see?

In this third part, you have used your sense of seeing to experience the static electric force. What have you learned about the static electric force from all three parts of this activity?

          © 2011 AIMS Education Foundation

Static Sensations

PART FOUR: AN ENLIGHTENING EXPERIENCE

What happens when you bring your charged balloon near the electrodes of a fluorescent light bulb?

electrodes — **fluorescent bulb**

Charge your balloon and slowly bring it near the electrodes on the bulb. Observe what happens. Be sure to bring various parts of the balloon near the electrodes. What did you observe?

Forces often move things. In this activity, what moved?

In some ways, this activity is similar to lightning. In what ways are these two things similar and in what ways are they different?

Summary:
What did you learn about the static electric force in all four parts of this activity?

Connecting Learning

Part One
1. What did you notice when you moved the charged balloon just above the back of your hand?

2. What did you notice when you moved the charged balloon just above the palm of your hand?

3. What did you notice when you moved the balloon around your head?

Part Two
1. What did you hear when you brought a paper clip near your charged balloon?

2. What did you hear when you brought other objects close to your charged balloon?

3. What can you tell about the static electric force from this experience?

Connecting Learning

Part Three

1. What did you see when you lowered your charged balloon over your paper?

2. What did you notice when you brought the balloon near various other materials?

3. What happened when you held your charged balloon next to the wall and let go?

Static Sensations

Connecting Learning

Part Four

1. What did you see when you brought your charged balloon near the electrodes of the fluorescent bulb?

2. What did you notice when you brought various parts of the balloon near the electrodes?

3. Forces often move things. In this activity, what moved?

4. Lightning is a powerful example of static electricity in nature. How is this experiment like lightning and how is it different?

5. What have you learned about the static electric force from all four parts of this activity?

6. What are you wondering now?

St. Elmo's Fire

Many years ago, when sailing ships traveled at night, a strange, bluish light dancing on the masts of their ships sometimes frightened sailors. The light was often accompanied by crackling noises. They named the effect St. Elmo's Fire after the patron saint of sailors.

In the years since, St. Elmo's Fire has become the unwanted companion of airplane pilots as well. They sometimes see St. Elmo's Fire when they fly near thunderstorms or cumulonimbus clouds. The light appears on the wings and propellers of airplanes, ships' masts, and other objects that are higher than their surroundings.

3

St. Elmo's Fire is not a fire at all. It is really a discharge of static electricity. Static electricity is called that to distinguish it from current electricity. Static electricity remains stationary until it builds up enough electric potential to discharge. The more familiar current electricity moves through electrical circuits in a steady, predictable manner.

Static electricity often builds up on tall objects when the atmosphere is full of electrical charges. That is why St. Elmo's Fire is most often seen and heard before or during a thunderstorm.

Static electricity can produce shocks, St. Elmo's Fire, lightning, and other serious problems.

In 1937, static electricity may have sparked the explosion of the hydrogen-filled airship Hindenburg as it was docking at Lakehurst, New Jersey.

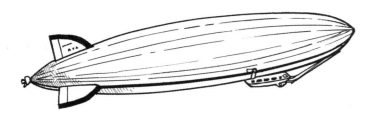

The Hindenburg
length: 245 meters (804 feet)
width: 41 meters (135 feet)
volume: 199,980 cubic meters (7,062,100 cubic feet)
cruising speed: 126 kilometers (78 miles) per hour

4

Balance Your Charge Account

Topic
Static electricity

Key Question
How can you balance the charges in an atom?

Learning Goal
Students will play a game reinforcing static electricity concepts.

Guiding Document
Project 2061 Benchmark
- *Without touching them, material that has been electrically charged pulls on all other materials and may either push or pull on other charged materials.*

Science
Physical science
  static electricity

Integrated Processes
Observing
Comparing and contrasting
Relating

Materials
For each group:
  game board
  one paper fastener
  one paper clip
  small objects of different colors (buttons or plastic chips) to use as game pieces, one per person
  crayons or markers

For each student:
  scissors

Background Information
This game reviews some of the ways that static electric charges can be produced on a balloon. When the game begins, the balloon is electrically balanced, since it has the same number of positive and negative charges. As the game is played, negative charges are gained and lost. If there are more negative charges than positive ones on the balloon, it has a negative charge. If there are more positive charges than negative, the balloon has a positive charge.

Management
1. This game provides a good review of static electric concepts. It should be played after students have done several hands-on activities with static electricity.
2. The game boards should be made ahead of time.
3. Laminate the game boards to make them last longer. Make a spinner with a large-headed paper fastener and a paper clip. Straighten the outside loop of the paper clip. Put the paper fastener through the loop that is left and then through the center of the spinner on the game board.

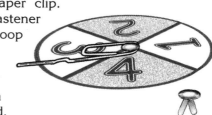

4. Students should be in groups of three or four.

Procedure
1. Distribute copies of *Balance Your Charges* and have students cut out the negative charges.
2. Distribute the game board and playing pieces to each group.
3. Have students select one game piece each and color the balloon on the activity sheet the same color.
4. Explain the rules and play the game. Announce or agree on a time period so that the person in each group with the most nearly balanced balloon can be declared the winner.
   a. Each player begins with a balanced balloon, equal numbers of positive and negative charges. Place a negative charge on top of each positive charge. Put the extra charges in the middle of the game board. Place playing pieces on GO.
   b. Students spin; the player with the highest number plays first. This player spins again, moves accordingly, reads the information on the space, and follows the directions. If the player gains negative charges, he/she draws them from the game board. If he/she loses negative charges, they are removed from his/her own balloon and added to the "pool" on the game board. If the player has extra negative charges, they are stored on his/her balloon.

 © 2011 AIMS Education Foundation

Connecting Learning

1. What makes a balloon balanced electrically?
2. What kind of static charge is on a balloon with more negative charges than positive ones?
3. What charge is on a balloon with more positive charges than negative ones?
4. What can make the balloon gain negative charges?
5. What can make the balloon lose negative charges?
6. How is this game like what happens with static electricity in the real world? How is it different?
7. What are you wondering now?

Extension

Have each group design new spaces for the game.

 **Your Charge Account**

Key Question

How can you balance the charges in an atom?

Learning Goal

play a game reinforcing static electricity concepts.

Balance − Your + Charges

© 2011 AIMS Education Foundation

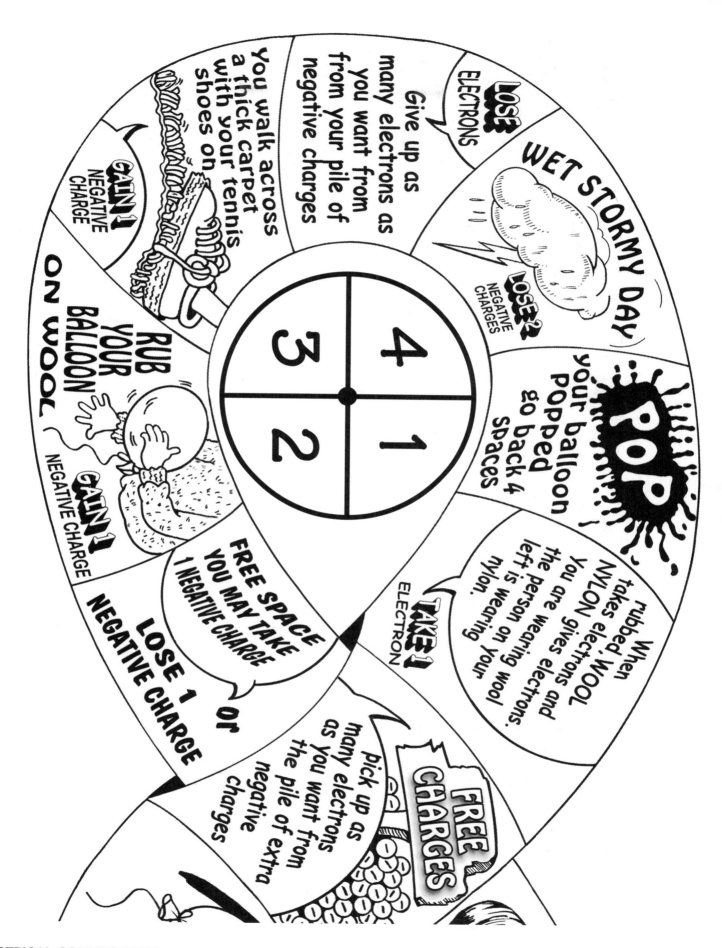

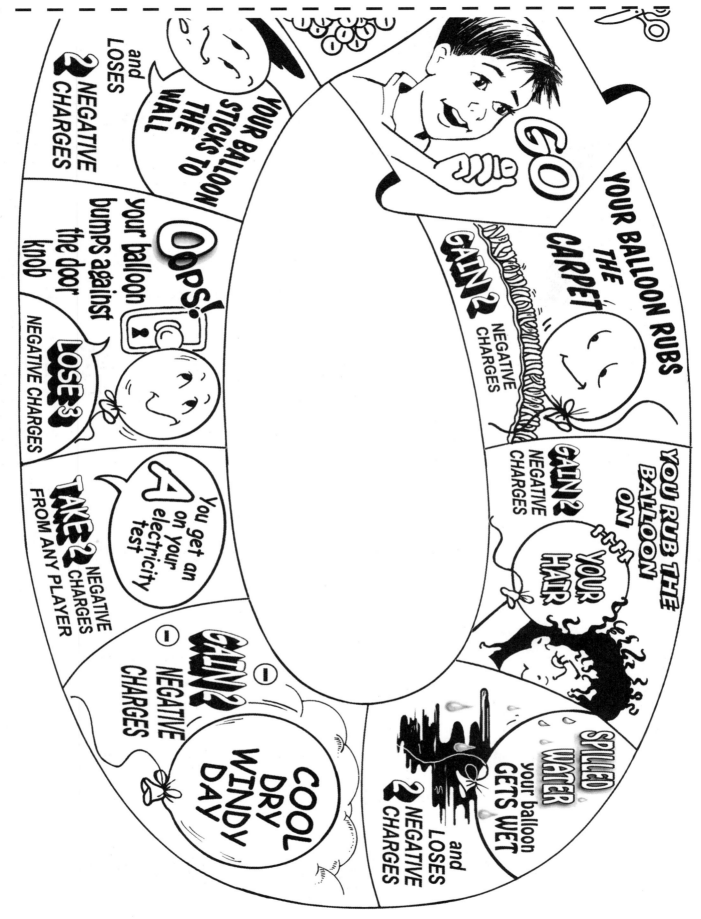

38

© 2011 AIMS Education Foundation

Balance Your Charge Account

Connecting Learning

1. What makes a balloon balanced electrically?

2. What kind of static charge is on a balloon with more negative charges than positive ones?

3. What charge is on a balloon with more positive charges than negative ones?

4. What can make the balloon gain negative charges?

5. What can make the balloon lose negative charges?

Balance Your Charge Account

Connecting Learning

6. How is this game like what happens with static electricity in the real world? How is it different?

7. What are you wondering now?

Nature's Light and Sound Show

Topic
Lightning—speed of light and sound

Key Question
When you see lightning and hear thunder, which reaches you first, the light or the sound?

Learning Goal
Students will determine how far away lightning is by counting the number of seconds between seeing the flash of lightning and hearing its thunder.

Guiding Documents
Project 2061 Benchmarks
- *Keep records of their investigations and observations and not change the records later.*
- *Something can be "seen" when light waves emitted or reflected by it enter the eye—just as something can be "heard" when sound waves from it enter the ear.*

NRC Standards
- *Ask a question about objects, organisms, and events in the environment.*
- *Use mathematics in all aspects of scientific inquiry.*

NCTM Standard 2000*
- *Carry out simple unit conversions, such as from centimeters to meters, within a system of measurement*

Math
Problem solving
Number and operations
    division
Measurement
    time

Science
Physical science
    static electricity
    sound
    light
Earth science
    weather
        thunder
        lightning

Integrated Processes
Observing
Collecting and recording data
Generalizing
Applying

Materials
Directional compass
Clock that ticks
Student pages
Calculators, optional

Background Information
The flash of light we see when lightning strikes travels at the speed of light. The lightning itself (which is electrical) travels just a bit more slowly. The speed of light is approximately 300,000 kilometers per second or 186,000 miles per second. The speed of light varies with the medium it is traveling through and is fastest in a vacuum. Light is slowed very slightly by air.

Thunder is caused by the shock wave that occurs when lightning superheats the air around it. Since thunder is sound, it travels at the speed of sound. The speed of sound is approximately 1200 kilometers per hour or 750 miles per hour. The speed of sound in air varies with the temperature, atmospheric pressure, and several other factors.

Since the flash and thunder caused by lightning occur almost simultaneously but travel at different speeds, the distance lightning is from an observer can be found by finding the difference in time between the flash and the thunder. Since the flash of lightning travels at such great speed (fast enough to travel around the world almost eight times in one second), we can say that it reaches a viewer almost instantaneously. The much slower thunder, which travels at the speed of sound, takes longer to reach an observer. When the flash of lightning is seen, the thunder will be traveling to the observer at about 1200 kilometers (750 miles) per hour. This is about 333 meters per second or a kilometer every three seconds (1100 feet per second or about a mile every five seconds).

To find how far away lightning is in kilometers, an observer counts the number of seconds between seeing the flash of lightning and hearing its thunder, then divides this number by three. For example, if there are 13 seconds between seeing the lightning and hearing its thunder, it would be a little over four

    41   © 2011 AIMS Education Foundation

kilometers away. To find the distance in miles, *the time would be divided by five.* Thus a difference of 15 seconds between the lightning and the thunder would mean that the lightning is about three miles away.

Management
1. Calculators can be used with this lesson.
2. This lesson was designed to be done using metric units. It can be done using standard units by substituting the equivalent values from the *Background Information.*
3. In tracking a storm with page three, use collaborative learning groups. We suggest the following roles:
   Student #1: observes lightning, calls out a prearranged signal, and points in that direction
   Student #2: on the chart draws a straight, colored line from the center out in that direction
   Student #3: at the signal, starts counting seconds until thunder is heard
   Student #4: records the number of seconds, computes the distance, and records this on the table
   Student #2: on the chart records a black "X" on the line at the approximate distance from the center.
4. Directional compasses (item number 1990) are available from AIMS.

Procedure
1. As a class, share information and experiences related to lightning and lightning storms. When the dangers of lightning are mentioned, agree that lightning can be dangerous because it is electrical, but that just as we use electricity and use it safely, we can observe and study lightning without danger. Caution students not to stand outdoors to observe lightning; if they are caught outdoors, they should go into a building.
2. Distribute the first two pages and discuss the *Key Question:* "When you see lightning and hear thunder, which reaches you first, the light or the sound?"
3. Work through the first page. The speed of light is commonly given in kilometers per second and the speed of sound in kilometers per hour. To compare the two, it is necessary for students to learn how to express them in the same terms. Have students calculate the distance sound travels per minute (20 km) and per second (1/3 or 0.33 km).
4. Work through the upper part of page two, guiding students as they start to realize the vast difference between the speeds of light and sound.

5. Storm simulation: In order to track a real lightning storm, students need to learn to count seconds with some degree of accuracy. Use a ticking clock to help them count "one one-thousand, two one-thousand..." until they can do this.
6. To simulate the lightning, flash the classroom lights. Students begin counting. Prepare some kind of noise to simulate the thunder. When the thunder sounds at three seconds, students record the three, *then* explain that they are dividing by three to compute the distance in kilometers. (Repeatedly help them to see that every *three second* gap between lightning flash and thunder represents one kilometer.)
7. Use page three to track a real storm. (See *Management* for student roles.) For safety, do this from indoors. If you do not have lightning storms in your area, you may simulate a storm in the same way that one was simulated using page two. Be sure to make the line colored and the "X" black, so that the chart does not become cluttered with marks. The important part of the chart is to see how the storm has moved by observing the pattern of *"X"s.* (We are indebted to Dr. Verne R. Rockcastle of Cornell University for this strategy of tracking storms.)

Connecting Learning
1. Which travels faster, light or sound?
2. How do you know?
3. What are some other examples where you see something before you hear it?
4. If you hear thunder at almost the same time that you see lightning, what does that tell you?
5. What are you wondering now?

Extensions
1. Do the activity substituting miles for kilometers.
2. Have students go to a track meet and calculate the speed of sound. This can be done if they stand a known distance from the starting gun and use a stopwatch. By watching for the puff of smoke from the gun and timing how long it takes to hear the bang, the speed of sound can be calculated.

Curriculum Correlation
Language Arts
Have students read more about lightning and write a report on their findings.

Social Studies
Research Benjamin Franklin and his study of lightning.

* Reprinted with permission from *Principles and Standards for School Mathematics,* 2000 by the National Council of Teachers of Mathematics. All rights reserved.

Nature's Light and Sound Show

Key Question

When you see lightning and hear thunder, which reaches you first, the light or the sound?

Learning Goal

Students will:

determine how far away lightning is by counting the number of seconds between seeing the flash of lightning and hearing its thunder.

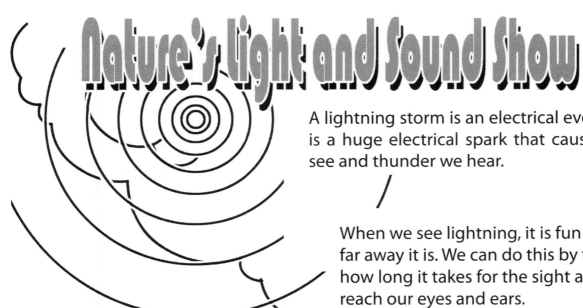

Nature's Light and Sound Show

A lightning storm is an electrical event. Lightning is a huge electrical spark that causes a flash we see and thunder we hear.

When we see lightning, it is fun to know how far away it is. We can do this by finding out how long it takes for the sight and sound to reach our eyes and ears.

Since light travels very fast, its speed is difficult to measure. Instead, we will work with the sound, the thunder.

Sound travels about 1200 **kilometers per hour**.

How far does sound travel per **minute**?
There are 60 minutes in each hour.
Divide 1200 by 60.

Sound travels about _____ **kilometers per minute**.

How far does sound travel per **second**?
There are 60 seconds in each minute.
Divide your **kilometers per minute** by 60.

Sound travels about _____ **kilometers per second**.

If light travels about 300,000 km per second and sound travels _____ km per second, which would reach you first?

Explain your answer.

44   © 2011 AIMS Education Foundation

Nature's Light and Sound Show

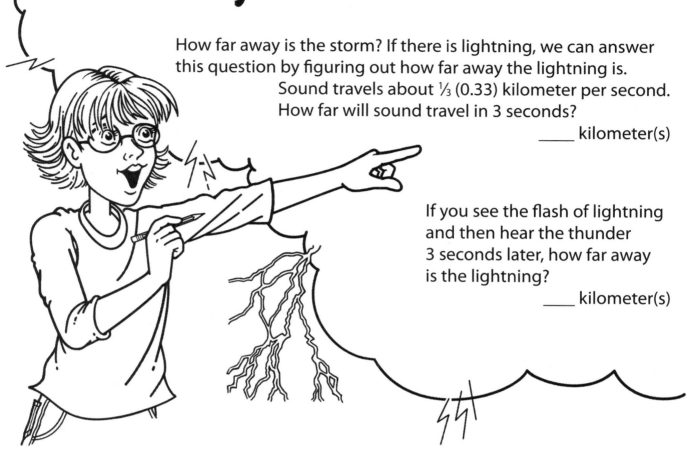

How far away is the storm? If there is lightning, we can answer this question by figuring out how far away the lightning is.

Sound travels about ⅓ (0.33) kilometer per second. How far will sound travel in 3 seconds?

_____ kilometer(s)

If you see the flash of lightning and then hear the thunder 3 seconds later, how far away is the lightning?

_____ kilometer(s)

Count the seconds between the flash of lightning and the sound of the thunder. Use this table to record your data.

Now let's practice tracking a storm.

Time between lightning and thunder (seconds)	÷ 3	Distance of lightning (km)
	÷ 3	
	÷ 3	
	÷ 3	

Congratulations!
You are a storm tracker!

Nature's Light and Sound Show

Let's track a real storm. Here is a chart and a table to help you.

1. Place the chart so that it is correctly aligned with north. When there is a flash of lightning, note the location. Is it north of you? ...southeast? ...west? Draw a colored line from the center (you) out in that direction.

Time (seconds)	÷ 3	Distance (km)
	÷ 3	
	÷ 3	
	÷ 3	
	÷ 3	
	÷ 3	
	÷ 3	
	÷ 3	

Each circle represents 1 km.

2. Count the seconds and find out how far away the lightning is. Record data on the table.
3. On the chart, put a black X on the line to show how far away the lightning is.
4. Continue to observe lightning and record its location. Remember, the lightning may not be in the center of the storm.

What did you learn?

© 2011 AIMS Education Foundation

Nature's Light and Sound Show

Connecting Learning

1. Which travels faster, light or sound?

2. How do you know?

3. What are some other examples where you see something before you hear it?

4. If you hear thunder at almost the same time that you see lightning, what does that tell you?

5. What are you wondering now?

          © 2011 AIMS Education Foundation

Lightning strikes somewhere on the Earth about 100 times each second. That means there are lots of opportunities to study it. People have even developed high-speed cameras to automatically photograph lightning when it happens.

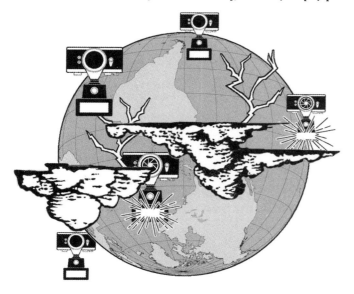

Lightning is a very interesting phenomenon of nature. It is a huge electrical spark—a kind of static electricity. We usually see it going from a cloud to the ground. It can also travel between two clouds, within a cloud, and even from a cloud into the air.

Although many scientists have investigated what it is and how it works, lightning is still very difficult to analyze and understand. We continue to study it and learn more.

Barometric Pressure

Wind velocity

Electric Field

ightning

Lightning strikes are very short—only about a millionth of a second. But, they have huge amounts of electric current. Some have been measured at over 300,000 amperes of electricity. That is enough to light about 200,000 homes!

Fulminologists don't know for sure how lightning forms. There are lots of different ideas. We do know that it has to do with positive and negative charges of particles in the air.

As lightning travels through the air, it heats the air in its path to around 20,000°C (36,000°F). That's about three times as hot as the surface of the sun! This superheated air expands very quickly, producing a wave of pressure that causes thunder.

The study of lightning is called *fulminology*. People who study lightning are called *fulminologists*.

Department of Fulminology

1. What do we really know about lightning?

STATIC EXTENSIONS

These activities work best in a cool, dry environment; otherwise, the static charges quickly dissipate.

Give each student a small 5 x 7 cm piece of scratch paper. Have them scuff their feet on a carpet and then place the paper flat against a vertical surface. Observe what happens. Repeat twice more with different surfaces. The paper will stick to some surfaces and not to others. When it sticks to a vertical surface, the charge on the paper induces an opposite charge in the surface to which it sticks.

Have students rub their hair (it should be clean and dry) with a balloon and hold the balloon near a thin, steady stream of water from a faucet. Observe the results. The negative charge on the balloon will induce a positive charge in the stream of water. The opposite charges attract, and the path of the water is bent toward the balloon.

Rub nylon stockings with plastic wrap. Observe what happens. The stockings will gain a positive charge and (since like charges repel) the stockings will "fill up."

Blow soap bubbles and attract them with a charged balloon.

Use static electricity to overcome gravity by sticking charged balloons on the wall or ceiling.

 © 2011 AIMS Education Foundation

Put a piece of paper on the wall and rub it with nylon and then plastic wrap; see which makes it stick to the wall the longest.

Rub various plastic straws or pens with nylon or a paper towel. Depending on the type of plastic they are made of, some will gain a strong negative charge and act as "magic wands," attracting salt, small bits of paper, Styrofoam, etc.

In a darkened room, pull some tape off a roll of electric tape; watch the static sparks.

Borrow a Van de Graaff generator from a high school science teacher and let your students have a hair-raising experience!

Hang a banana from a string. Charge a balloon and bring it near the banana. The balloon will induce an opposite charge in the near part of the banana. If the balloon is moved around the banana, the banana will rotate and follow the balloon.

© 2011 AIMS Education Foundation

Topic
Electrical circuits

Key Question
How can you make a bulb light using only a bulb, a D cell, and a jumbo paper clip or wire?

Learning Goals
Students will:
- discover how to make a complete circuit that lights a bulb using only a D cell, a bulb, and a jumbo paper clip; and
- observe the transformation of chemical energy into light and/or heat energy.

Guiding Documents
Project 2061 Benchmarks
- *Make safe electrical connections with various plugs, sockets, and terminals.*
- *Make sketches to aid in explaining procedures or ideas.*

NRC Standards
- *Employ simple equipment and tools to gather data and extend the senses.*
- *Electricity in circuits can produce light, heat, sound, and magnetic effects. Electrical circuits require a complete loop through which an electrical current can pass.*

Science
Physical science
    electricity
       circuits
    energy transformation

Integrated Processes
Observing
Comparing and contrasting
Generalizing

Materials
For each group:
    plastic bag containing:
        D cell
        flashlight bulb
        jumbo paper clip

For each student:
    student page

Background Information
If a flashlight bulb is placed correctly in a complete circuit so that electricity passes through it, it will light. In order for current to flow through the bulb, it must be connected to the circuit at two points, the *tip contact* (the metal button at the bottom of the bulb) and the *base contact* (the metal side of the bulb's base). To make the bulb light with the materials listed, either the base contact or the tip contact of the bulb must touch one terminal of the D cell (battery). The paper clip or wire must connect the cell's other terminal to the remaining contact. One way to do this is shown in the illustration.

This activity exemplifies the transformation of energy. Of course the ideal transformation is from the chemical energy that is stored in the D cell to light energy as the bulb glows. However, with students' initial efforts, they will most likely experience the transformation of chemical energy to heat energy as the wire heats. The hot wire will certainly startle students, and they should be told to disconnect the wire. If students leave the wire connected in such a fashion, they will succeed only in making the wire hot—too hot to handle—and in draining the battery of its chemical energy.

Management
1. Students should be in groups of two.
2. Test bulbs and cells beforehand to be sure they are working. Bulbs (item number 1962) are available from AIMS.
3. The cells, bulbs, and paper clips should be put into bags ahead of time. Each group receives one bag.

Procedure
1. Distribute a plastic bag and the activity pages to each group.
2. Challenge the students to make the bulb light using only the materials in the bag. Caution the students to release the paper clip if it gets hot.

3. After students have made the bulb light, challenge them to find another way to light the bulb using the same materials.
4. Make sure that no students leave the paper clip attached to both terminals of the cell.
5. Have students draw pictures showing two ways they lit their bulbs.
6. Discuss the results and the energy transformations that took place.

Connecting Learning
1. How many ways can we light the bulb with these materials?
2. What other materials could we use instead of the paper clip? [wire, aluminum foil, etc.]
3. Do you think the bulb will light with a different size cell? Explain.
4. How many places on the cell did you have to connect? Where were they? [two, the top of the cell and the bottom]
5. How many places on the bulb did you have to connect? Where were they? [two, the side of the metal band on the bulb and the very bottom tip of the bulb]
6. What does making a complete circuit mean? How was your method of lighting the bulb a complete circuit?
7. What forms of energy did you observe? [chemical, light, and heat]
8. How did the energy transform from one form to another? [The chemical energy in the battery was transformed to light energy when the bulb was lit. Some was also transformed into heat energy that we could feel in the wire.]
9. What are you wondering now?

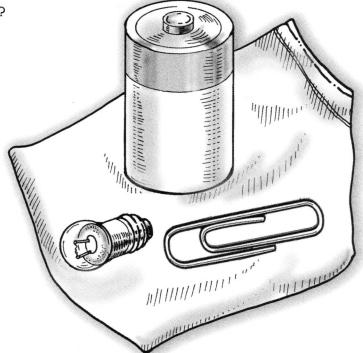

SPARKY'S LIGHT KIT

Key Question

How can you make a bulb light using only a bulb, a D cell, and a jumbo paper clip?

Learning Goals

Students will:

- discover how to make a complete circuit that lights a bulb using only a D cell, a bulb, and a jumbo paper clip; and

- observe the transformation of chemical energy into light and/or heat energy.

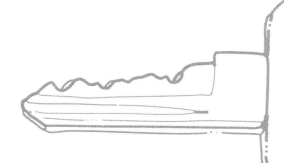

© 2011 AIMS Education Foundation

SPARKY'S LIGHT KIT

Complete
a circuit
using only:
• a battery
• a paper clip
• a bulb

Draw pictures that show two ways you lit the bulb.

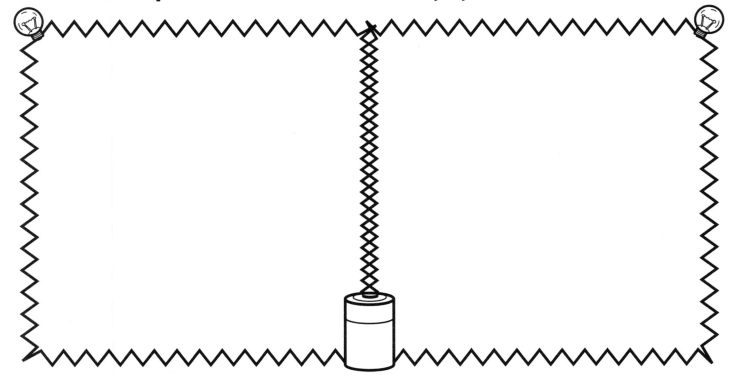

SPARKY'S LIGHT KIT

Connecting Learning

1. How many ways can we light the bulb with these materials?

2. What other materials could we use instead of the paper clip?

3. Do you think the bulb will light with a different size cell? Explain.

4. How many places on the cell did you have to connect? Where were they?

5. How many places on the bulb did you have to connect? Where were they?

Connecting Learning

6. What does making a complete circuit mean? How was your method of lighting the bulb a complete circuit?

7. What forms of energy did you observe?

8. How did the energy transform from one form to another?

9. What are you wondering now?

Path Finders

Topic
Electrical circuits

Key Question
How can you make a complete electrical circuit that will light a bulb?

Learning Goals
Students will:
- learn about complete and incomplete circuits by trying to light a bulb using various systems of bulbs, wires, and cells (batteries); and
- write instructions that others can follow.

Guiding Documents
Project 2061 Benchmarks
- *Make safe electrical connections with various plugs, sockets, and terminals.*
- *Make sketches to aid in explaining procedures or ideas.*
- *Write instructions that others can follow in carrying out a procedure.*

NRC Standard
- *Electricity in currents can produce light, heat, sound, and magnetic effects. Electrical circuits require a complete loop through which an electrical current can pass.*

Science
Physical science
electricity
circuits

Integrated Processes
Observing
Predicting
Collecting and recording data
Organizing data
Drawing conclusions
Communicating

Materials
For each group:
D cell
bulb
two 10-15 cm wires (see *Management 5*)
scissors
red and yellow crayons or markers
glue stick

For each student:
student pages

Background Information
A complete circuit is a series of wires and/or electrical devices that form a closed path through which electricity can flow. To work, a circuit needs a source of electrical energy. The source of electricity used in this investigation is the chemical energy in the cell, better known to most people as a battery. (A cell is a single unit containing electrodes and an electrolyte for producing electricity. A battery is made up of two or more cells joined together.)

If an incandescent bulb is placed in a complete circuit so that the electricity passes through it, it will light. Incandescent bulbs have two thick wires supporting a thin, tightly coiled, conducting filament that glows when electricity flows through it. (Edison's original bulb used sewing thread for the filament!) To make the bulb a part of the circuit, one of the circuit wires must be touching the bottom tip of the bulb's base, and the other must touch the metal side of the bulb's base. Any system that causes the bulb to light is a complete circuit.

Management
1. *Sparky's Light Kit* may be used before this activity to provide some experience with circuits.
2. This activity works best if students work in groups of two or three.
3. Beforehand, make sure that all the cells and bulbs are functioning.
4. Although D cells work best for this activity, C or AA cells can also be used.

5. Insulation should be stripped off about two centimeters at the ends of the wires so that a good connection can be made. Narrow strips of aluminum foil that have been backed with masking tape can be substituted for the wire.
6. Bulbs (item number 1962), insulated wire (item number 1967), and wire strippers (item number 1970) are available from AIMS.

Procedure
Part One
1. Show students a cell, two wires, and a bulb. Discuss the *Key Question:* How can you make a complete electric circuit that will light a bulb?
2. Give each group a cell, wires, and a bulb; challenge them to get their bulb to light. Allow time for exploration so that students may test various circuits. Help any groups that have trouble.
3. Have each successful group show and explain what they did.
4. Hand out the yellow and red crayons and the first student page. Have students predict which of the pictured systems will light by drawing a red star on them.
5. Have students build each system pictured and observe whether or not it lights the bulb. (Diagrams A, E, G, and H depict complete circuits.) Tell students to color a yellow star on the diagram of each arrangement that worked.
6. When groups have finished testing all the systems, discuss the results.

Part Two
1. Distribute scissors, glue sticks, and the second and third student pages. Explain that students should cut out each of the systems on the left half of the second sheet and glue them on the third sheet, putting diagrams of complete circuits in *The Bulb Hut* store and incomplete circuits in *Sparky's Fix It Shop*.
2. Have each group think how Sparky can make the incomplete circuits work. Groups can test these predictions and draw in the necessary changes.

Part Three
1. Hand out the last student page, *Repair Manual*. Have groups cut out the pictures of the circuits that won't light and glue them in the *Repair Manual*. Let the groups discuss why the systems pictured won't work and then how they could be fixed. Tell students to record this information on the sheet, using illustrations and written instructions. Encourage the students to follow their written instructions to see if they are clear and correct.

2. As a class, share methods of fixing each of the non-working systems. Let students check the instructions by manipulating their systems as groups read their solutions.

Connecting Learning
1. What are the similarities of the systems that work?
2. What are the similarities of the systems that don't work?
3. Is electricity flowing through the systems that make the bulbs light? How do you know?
4. Is electricity flowing through the systems that don't make the bulbs light? How do you know?
5. What do you think are necessary elements of all complete circuits?
6. Which was easier—illustrating the repairs or writing the repair manual? Explain why you think one was more difficult.
7. What are you wondering now?

Extensions
1. Make as many different complete circuits as possible using the materials provided.
2. Test other materials that can be substituted for the wire.
3. Make a switch that turns the bulb on and off.
4. Use a battery (two or more cells linked together) as a part of the circuit and note the difference in the brightness of the bulb. Warn students that bulbs burn out more quickly when more cells are added.

Curriculum Correlation
Language Arts
Write a story about working in *Sparky's Fix It Shop.*

Social Studies
Discuss how the electric light has changed our daily life. Read about how the light bulb was invented. Read a biography of Thomas Edison. What else did he invent? Since he is thought to have had a learning disability, discuss his achievements in the light of these difficulties.

Path Finders

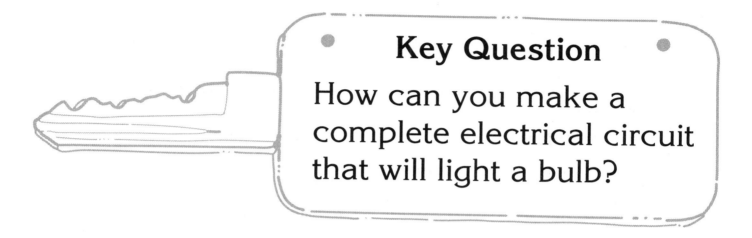

Key Question

How can you make a complete electrical circuit that will light a bulb?

Learning Goals

Students will:

- learn about complete and incomplete circuits by trying to light a bulb using various systems of bulbs, wires, and cells (batteries); and

- write instructions that others can follow.

Path Finders

1. Predict which bulbs will light by making a red star beside them.
2. Make a yellow star on all those that really did light.

Path Finders

Repair Manual

Cutouts

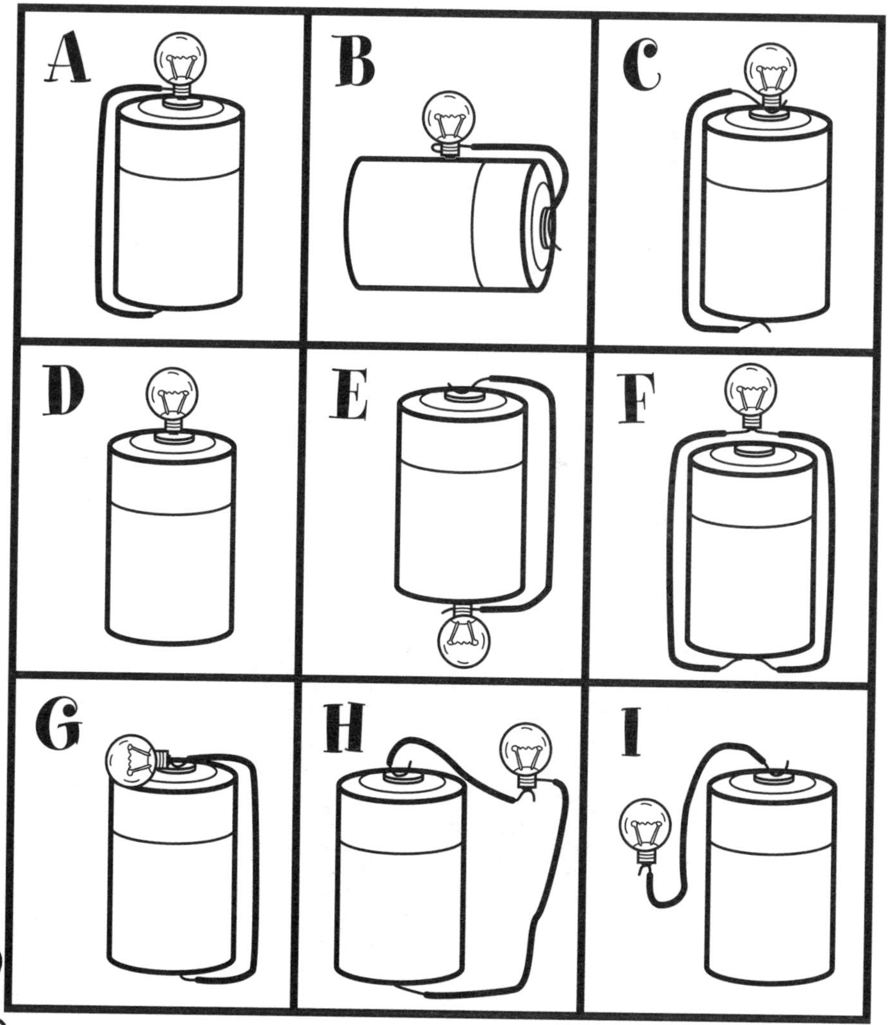

A	B	C
D	E	F
G	H	I

The Bulb Hut

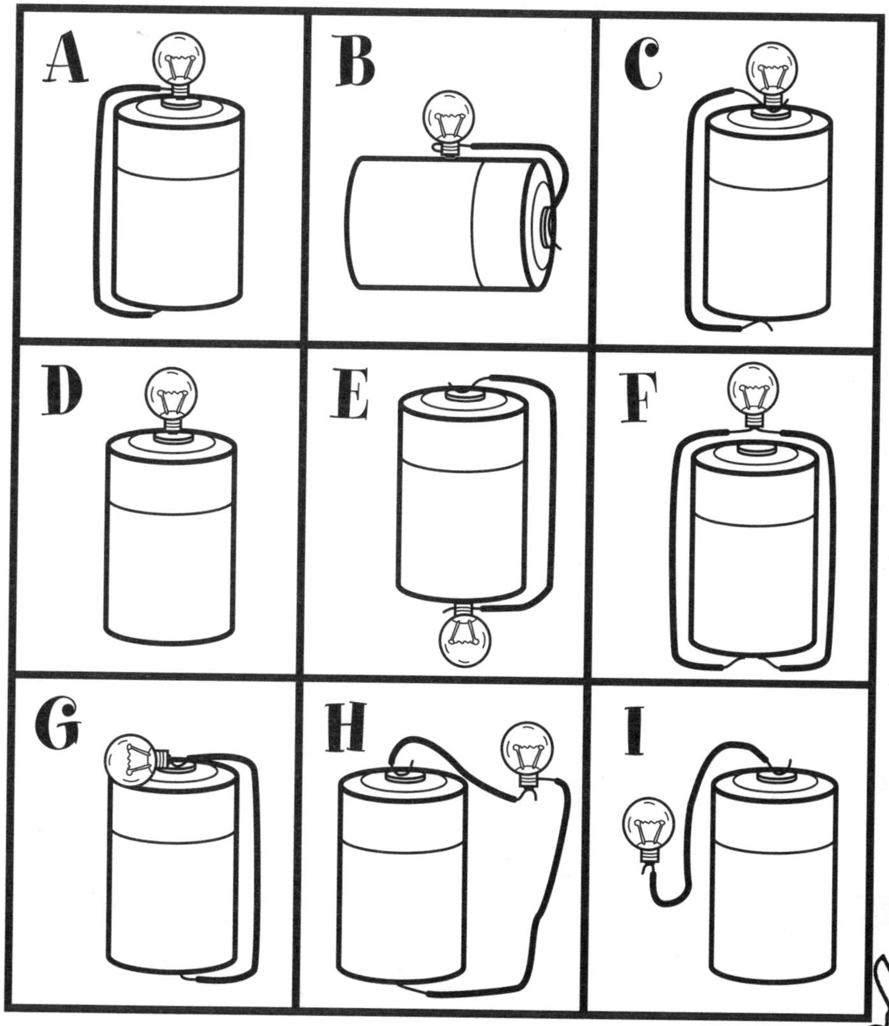

SPARKY's Fix It Shop

Cutouts

A	B	C
D	E	F
G	H	I

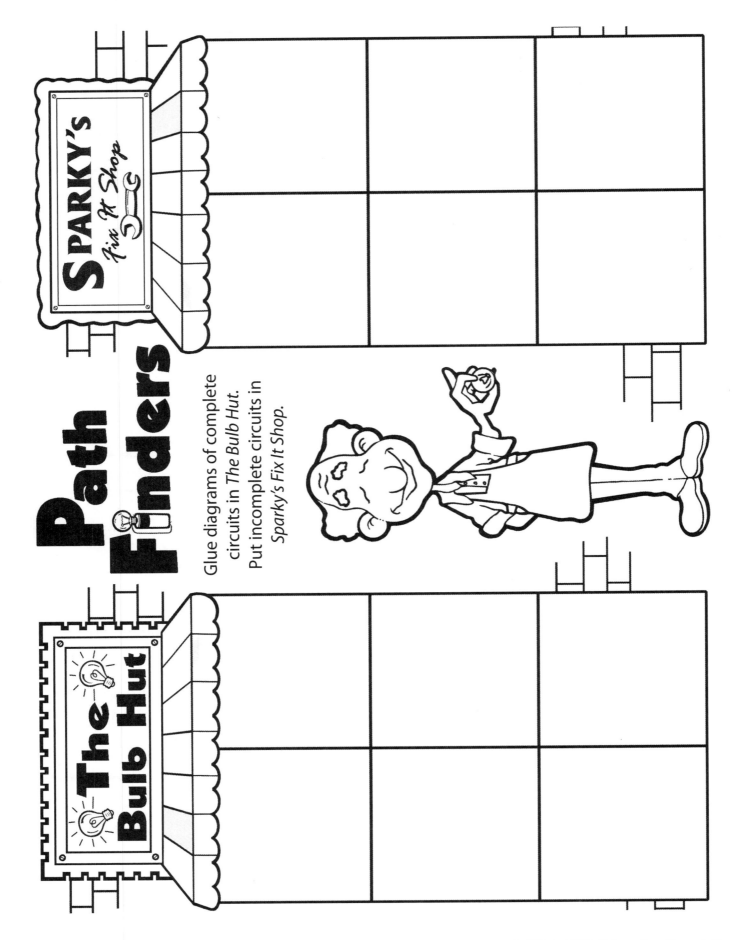

Path Finders

Glue diagrams of complete circuits in *The Bulb Hut*. Put incomplete circuits in *Sparky's Fix It Shop*.

SPARKY's
Fix It Shop

The Bulb Hut

Path Finders

Describe how to repair each system.

Repair Manual

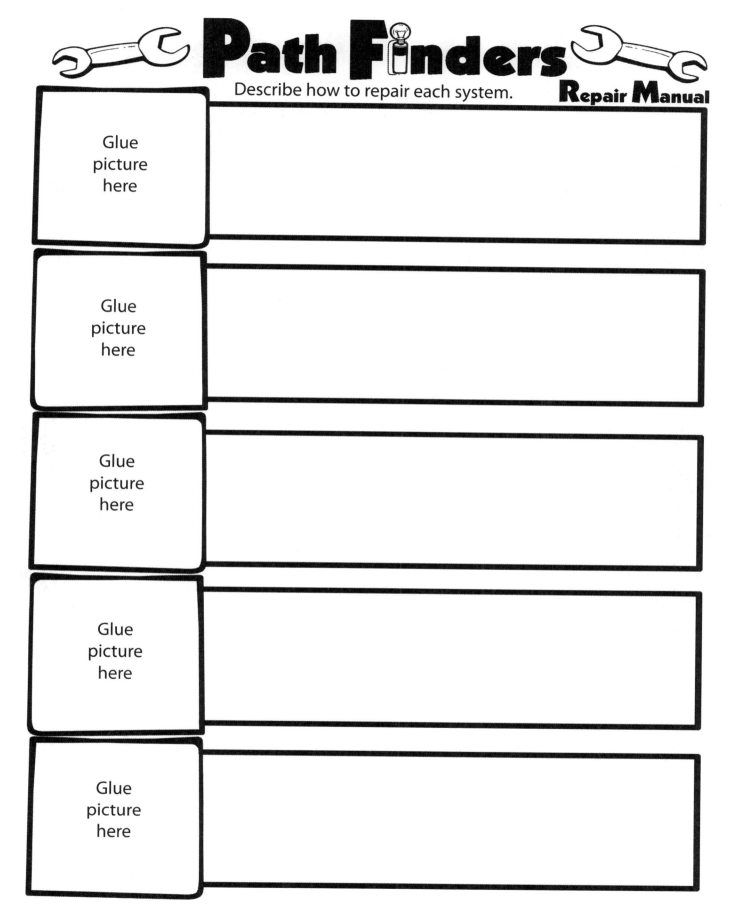

Glue picture here

Glue picture here

Glue picture here

Glue picture here

Glue picture here

© 2011 AIMS Education Foundation

Path Finders

Connecting Learning

1. What are the similarities of the systems that work?

2. What are the similarities of the systems that don't work?

3. Is electricity flowing through the systems that make the bulbs light? How do you know?

4. Is electricity flowing through the systems that don't make the bulbs light? How do you know?

5. What do you think are necessary elements of all complete circuits?

Path Finders

Connecting Learning

6. Which was easier—illustrating the repairs or writing the repair manual? Explain why you think one was more difficult.

7. What are you wondering now?

© 2011 AIMS Education Foundation

CIRCUIT QUIZ CARDS

Topic
Electrical circuits

Key Question
What makes our quiz cards light when we match the question to its answer?

Learning Goals
Students will:
- make circuit quiz cards,
- write questions and answers to put on the cards, and
- determine the paths of the circuits on the cards.

Guiding Documents
Project 2061 Benchmark
- *Make safe electrical connections with various plugs, sockets, and terminals.*

NRC Standard
- *Electricity in circuits can produce light, heat, sound, and magnetic effects. Electrical circuits require a complete loop through which an electrical current can pass.*

Science
Physical science
    electricity
        circuits

Integrated Processes
Observing
Comparing and contrasting
Inferring
Applying

Materials
Per circuit card:
    2 index cards, 5" x 7"
    1 D cell
    1 battery holder
    small bulb
    bulb holder
    insulated wire (see *Management 5*)
    wire stripper, optional (see *Management 5*)
    ruler, optional (see *Management 5*)
    hole punch
    4 paper clips
    aluminum foil, 30 cm (1 ft)
    masking tape

Background Information
Each question of the circuit quiz card is connected to the correct answer by a strip of aluminum foil that conducts the electricity like a wire. The back side of the aluminum foil is covered by masking tape to insulate it and prevent short circuits. When a correct question and answer are chosen, it completes the circuit, causing the bulb to light.

Management
1. Have a sample of the quiz card made up beforehand to show students how it is constructed.
2. If index cards are not available, cut card stock into 5" x 7" pieces.
3. Hole punches can be shared.
4. Aluminum foil wires can be made ahead of time or students can make them as part of the project. (See the *Construction* pages.)
5. Insulated wires are needed for making the electrical tester. Each student or group will need two wires 30-35 cm long with the ends stripped. They will also need a short piece that is about 8 cm long with ends stripped. These wires can be prepared ahead of time or students can cut and strip them. If students are preparing the wires, they will need a wire stripper and a ruler.
6. You may have students work individually or in groups to research the questions and construct the quiz cards. The topics for the questions/answers can come from any content area (math facts, science content, geography, etc.). Students can work on the questions/answers as homework. They should prepare six questions and their answers. If they want, they can prepare more than one set of six questions/answers. In such cases, give them extra question/answer sheets. They should arrange the questions and answers to match the schematic that they drew at the beginning of the lesson.
7. Set up an area in the classroom with the supplies that are needed for making the quiz cards. Students can then go to this area to pick up and return their supplies.
8. The following items are available from AIMS: bulb holders (item number 1958), battery holders (item number 1960), bulbs (item number 1962), wire (item number 1968), and wire strippers (item number 1970).

Procedure

1. Show students a sample quiz card and demonstrate how it works. Tell students that they will be building similar cards. Discuss how the quiz cards work.

2. Inform them that they will need to write out six questions and answers that will be used on the quiz card. Let them know that these will be needed the following day. If appropriate, assign the topics that can be used for generating questions.

3. Distribute the first student page. Assign each student or group a card number. Have them record this number on the schematic and on the quiz card portion of the page.

4. Discuss the schematic that is found at the top of the page. Tell students that they need to plan which holes on their circuit quiz card they are going to connect. Direct them to draw these in. Emphasize that students will need to refer to this schematic as they make and test their circuit quiz cards.

5. Distribute the *Construction* pages. Show the students the materials center. Allow time for students to read and follow the directions. Assist as needed in the construction and testing process.

6. After students have tested their cards to make sure they work correctly, collect the cards. Distribute the last student page. Hand cards randomly to students. Have them record the card number and determine and record the paths they infer the wires to make. Students or groups should test four different cards.

7. Allow time for students to compare their answers to the schematics of the students or groups that constructed the cards.

Connecting Learning

1. Why does the bulb light when the two wires touch the right question and answer? [A circuit was completed.]

2. How can you use the same card for other sets of questions and answers? [You have to make sure to put the answers in the areas that are connected to the questions.]

3. Why is the masking tape so important? [It prevents short circuits.]

4. How do you think the quiz card is like the wiring in a house?

5. What could be wrong if the question and its answer don't light up? [The question could be connected to the wrong area for its answer. There could be some aluminum foil touching another foil wire and causing a short circuit. The tester bulb and battery may not be connected correctly. Etc.]

6. Why might your light go on when a wrong answer is selected? [The wire for the question may go to the wrong answer area. A short circuit can join several answers to the same question. Etc.]

7. If you were to make another quiz card, what would you do differently?

8. What are you wondering now?

CIRCUIT QUIZ CARDS

Key Question

What makes our quiz cards light when we match the question to its answer?

Learning Goals

- make circuit quiz cards,
- write questions and answers to put on the cards, and
- determine the paths of the circuits on the cards.

CIRCUIT QUIZ CARDS

Card #	Questions	Answers	
A ●			1 ●
B ●			2 ●
C ●			3 ●
D ●			4 ●
E ●			5 ●
F ●			6 ●

Write your assigned number on the card to the left and on the one below.

Draw lines on the card to the left that represent your plan for the questions and answers you will write. This is your schematic. (A schematic is a diagram of a plan.)

Write your questions and answers on the card below to match the schematic you made.

Cut around the perimeter of the card.

Card #	Questions	Answers	
A ●			**1** ●
B ●			**2** ●
C ●			**3** ●
D ●			**4** ●
E ●			**5** ●
F ●			**6** ●

CIRCUIT QUIZ CARDS
CONSTRUCTION

You will need:

Aluminum foil
2 index cards (5" x 7")

Masking tape
4 paper clips

Hole punch
Scissors

Do this:

1. Make wires for your quiz card by putting strips of masking tape on a piece of aluminum foil. Tear or cut the strips apart. Trim off any exposed edges of aluminum foil. You will need at least six wires.

2. Cut out the quiz card. Place it on top of one of your index cards. Use four paper clips to hold it in place.

Card #	Questions	Answers	
A			1
B			2
C			3
D			4
E			5
F			6

3. Use a paper punch to make the 12 holes where indicated.

4. Place this card with holes on top of the second index card. Use your pencil to trace around the holes. Remove the first card and label the holes you drew on the second card (A-F and 1-6).

Card #	Questions	Answers	
A			1
B			2
C			3
D			4
E			5
F			6

© 2011 AIMS Education Foundation

5. Draw guidelines on the second card to match the schematic you drew.

6. Tape the aluminum foil wires over the guidelines you drew, connecting the lettered holes to the numbered holes. Do one wire at a time.

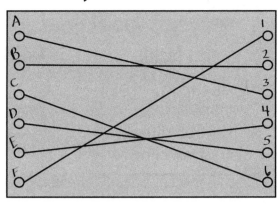

- Place a foil wire over one of the guidelines so that the foil extends beyond the hole. Trim the ends as necessary.

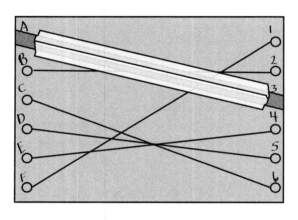

- Tape over the foil wire so that the only aluminum foil that is exposed is found where the holes are located. Any foil that is not covered by tape is a possible site for a short circuit.

- Repeat this process with each guideline until all are covered.

- When taping is finished, no foil should be visible except the ends on top of the hole marks you drew.

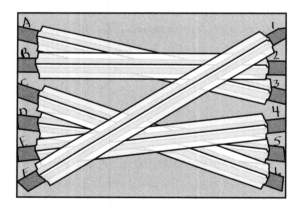

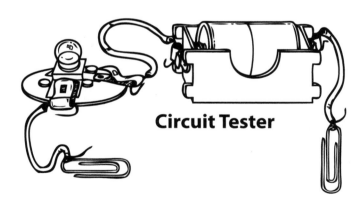

Circuit Tester

Set up the circuit tester as illustrated. To see if your quiz card works correctly, test the connections. To do this, connect the A to its corresponding numbered section you drew in your schematic. The bulb should light. If it doesn't, you have a problem. Also check A with the other numbered areas to make sure there is no light when they are connected. If the other numbered areas light, you have a problem.

Card #	Questions	Answers	
A			1
B			2
C			3
D			4
E			5
F			6

 © 2011 AIMS Education Foundation

Choose four different cards. Record the card number for each. Test the question and answers. Draw lines to show the circuits for each card.

Card #	Questions	Answers
A		1
B		2
C		3
D		4
E		5
F		6

Card #	Questions	Answers
A		1
B		2
C		3
D		4
E		5
F		6

Card #	Questions	Answers
A		1
B		2
C		3
D		4
E		5
F		6

Card #	Questions	Answers
A		1
B		2
C		3
D		4
E		5
F		6

Check your circuit diagrams with the schematics for each card. Do they match? Explain.

If there are differences between your diagrams and their schematics, what do you think caused the differences?

 © 2011 AIMS Education Foundation

CIRCUIT QUIZ CARDS

Connecting Learning

1. Why does the bulb light when the two wires touch the right question and answer?

2. How can you use the same card for other sets of questions and answers?

3. Why is the masking tape so important?

4. How do you think the quiz card is like the wiring in a house?

5. What could be wrong if the question and its answer don't light up?

CIRCUIT QUIZ CARDS

Connecting Learning

6. Why might your light go on when a wrong answer is selected?

7. If you were to make another quiz card, what would you do differently?

8. What are you wondering now?

 © 2011 AIMS Education Foundation

Fiddling With Filaments

Topic
Electricity

Key Question
What can we learn about the incandescent light bulb by studying a model light bulb?

Learning Goals
Students will:
- construct a model light bulb, and
- test a variety of materials as filaments to see which materials will glow.

Guiding Documents
Project 2061 Benchmarks
- *Scientific investigations may take many different forms, including observing what things are like or what is happening somewhere, collecting specimens for analysis, and doing experiments. Investigations can focus on physical, biological, and social questions.*
- *Things that give off light often also give off heat. Heat is produced by mechanical and electrical machines, and any time one thing rubs against something else.*
- *Seeing how a model works after changes are made to it may suggest how the real thing would work if the same were done to it.*
- *Science is an adventure that people everywhere can take part in, as they have for many centuries.*

NRC Standards
- *Scientific investigations involve asking and answering a question and comparing the answer with what scientists already know about the world.*
- *Electricity in circuits can produce light, heat, sound, and magnetic effects. Electrical circuits require a complete loop through which an electrical current can pass.*
- *Science and technology have been practiced by people for a long time.*
- *Men and women have made a variety of contributions throughout the history of science and technology.*

Science
Physical science
  electricity

Integrated Processes
Observing
Collecting and recording data
Comparing and contrasting
Communicating
Predicting
Identifying and controlling variables
Inferring

Materials
For each group:
  28-gauge wire (see *Management 1*)
  two 20-gauge copper wires, 15 cm each
  clay
  baby food jar
  cardboard, 6-cm square
  bell wire
  steel wool (see *Management 4*)
  incandescent light bulb

For the class:
  6-volt lantern battery
  alligator clips (see *Management 2*)
  book about Thomas Edison
    (see *Curriculum Correlation*)
  small bulb
  bulb holder

For each student:
  rubber band book
  #19 rubber band
  student pages

Background Information
Humphry Davy experimented with electricity and invented an electric battery in 1800. When he connected wires and a piece of carbon to his battery, the carbon glowed (incandesced), producing the first human-made electric light. Many years later, Thomas Alva Edison experimented with thousands of different filaments to find just the right materials that would glow well and be long lasting.

In this activity, students will construct model light bulbs and experiment with various metals as Edison did to find which materials make the best filaments. The filaments will light or not light because of resistance, a force that tends to oppose or retard motion. Students will have experienced resistance if they have ever walked through water. Water creates a greater resistance than air, making it harder to walk through. They get hot and may even turn red if they walk far enough in deep water. As students experiment with various light bulb filaments, the electricity flow will encounter different amounts of resistance as it passes through the metals. The resistance that it encounters is based on the type of metal and diameter of the wire. As the electric current passes through the wires, it makes the wires warm. If the electric current meets enough resistance, the wire will get so hot that it glows red- or even white-hot.

Management

1. Picture frame wire works well and can be purchased at a local department store. The wire comes as several strands wound together; these strands should be unwound before distributing them to the students.
2. Paper clips can be used in place of alligator clips, or the wires can simply be held so that the exposed metals touch.
3. If the wire (filament) glows too brightly and burns through too fast, suggest that students use a longer piece of wire (more ohms), or replace your 6-volt battery with two or three D-cells hooked in series (less volts).
4. It is suggested that you allow students to test the following wires for filaments: steel wool (thicker gauge and not copper), copper wire, picture frame wire, bell wire, paper clips, small thin finishing nails, wire strands from inside an old lamp cord, and springs from ball point pens.
5. **Don't connect a wire across the terminals of a 6-volt battery. It makes the battery get hot and drains its energy. It also makes the wire hot, and can cause burns and possible fires. It can make lithium batteries boil inside and burst.**
6. Prior to the lesson, prepare a testing area by stripping both ends of two 24-cm pieces of bell wire and attaching one end of one wire to the positive pole of the 6-volt battery and one end of the other wire to the negative pole of the battery. To test each filament, you will touch the free ends of these wires to the two copper wires on the student model bulb. For safety purposes, use one battery source to test light bulbs. The testing area should be managed by the teacher. You may choose to set up more than one of the battery sources to allow multiple groups to perform tests at one time.

7. To demonstrate that all of the metals being tested will conduct electricity, attach a bulb holder (item number 1958), bulb (item number 1962), and third wire (item number 1968) to the 6-volt battery as shown.

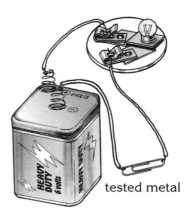

tested metal

8. Select a book about Thomas Edicson to read to the class. See *Curriculum Correlation* for suggestions.

Procedure

1. If possible, read and discuss the chapter(s) about Edison's search for a suitable filament material from one of the books listed in the *Curriculum Correlation*.
2. Explain that even though Thomas Edison is often credited with inventing the light bulb, there were many others who also played an important role. Distribute copies of the rubber band book on the history of the light bulb. Allow time for the students to read the book.
3. Ask the students what part of the light bulb scientists worked hardest to improve, based on their reading. [filament] Discuss why they think scientists put so much time and energy into developing the filament.
4. Distribute a commercial incandescent light bulb and the student pages to each group. Ask the students to observe the bulb. Instruct them to make a sketch of the light bulb and record their observations on the student recording sheet.
5. Tell the students that they will be constructing a model light bulb. Distribute one baby food jar, a golf-ball-sized ball of clay, one 6-centimeter square of cardboard, and two 15-centimeter pieces of copper wire to each group.
6. Have the groups soften the clay by rolling it around in their hands. When the clay is pliable, instruct them to flatten it into a pancake and place it onto the cardboard square.

7. Tell the students to form a loop in one end of each of the two copper wires. Have them bend the wires approximately 5 cm from the loop to form an "L." Have the students place the two copper wires into the clay so that the loops are about 3 cm apart and the ends with no loops are on opposite sides of the cardboard square.

8. Ask the students to invert the jar and carefully place it over the copper wires. Have the students sketch their model light bulbs on the recording sheet. Tell them to observe and record similarities and differences between the model and the commercial bulb. Ask the students what is missing from their models. [filament]
9. Explain to the students that they will be testing different materials to see what makes the best filament.
10. Show the students the power source that you will be using to test bulbs.
11. Gather the class around the battery. Display the materials they will be testing as possible filaments for their bulbs. Show the students that each metal being tested is a good conductor of electricity by touching the loose ends of the circuit containing the bulb and bulb holder to the ends of each metal. The bulb should light each time, demonstrating that the metal is a good conductor of electricity.
12. Distribute approximately 6 cm of each of the suggested wires, a paper clip, a finishing nail, etc.
13. Explain to the students that they will be attaching the filament to the two loops of the copper wire. Tell them they may choose to make a coil out of the wires they are testing by wrapping it around the end of a small wire and then sliding it off, or they may choose to leave the wire straight when they attach it.
14. When each group has its bulb prepared with one of the filaments, allow them to bring it to the testing area. Have them attach the wires to their copper wires and observe the results. Ask the group to then return to their desks, record their results, and prepare the next filament.
15. When all groups have tested all of the materials, ask them to decide which burned the longest and which gave off the brightest light. Discuss their results. Note similarities in those that glowed. [thin, silver, etc.]

Connecting Learning

1. How was your model light bulb similar to a commercially made bulb? ...different?
2. Which filament material created the brightest light? ...longest lasting light?
3. What problems, if any, did you encounter while trying to get the bulb to light?
4. What did you learn from this experience?
5. What, if anything, surprised you about the materials that you tested?
6. Why was it necessary that the filament be a conductor? [so electricity would flow through it, creating a circuit]
7. In what other electrical devices have you seen filaments that glow? [toasters, blow dryers, etc.] How are these devises like a light bulb? [The filaments glow. They have completed circuits. Etc.] How are they different? [They are used for heat rather than light.]
8. What are you wondering now?

Extension

Encourage students to look for other items that would make good filaments. Allow them to bring them in and test them.

Curriculum Correlation

Burgan, Michael. *Thomas Alva Edison: Great American Inventor.* Compass Point Books. Mankato, MN. 2007.

Egan, Louise. *Thomas Edison: The Great American Inventor.* Barron's Educational Series. New York. 1987.

Frith, Margaret. *Who Was Thomas Alva Edison?* Grosset & Dunlap. New York. 2005.

Fiddling With Filaments

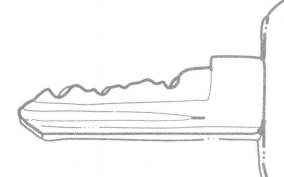

Key Question

What can we learn about the incandescent light bulb by studying a model light bulb?

Learning Goals

Students will:

- construct a model light bulb, and

- test a variety of materials as filaments to see which materials will glow.

Who Turned on the Lights?

In 1903, **Willis Whitnew** invented a metal-coated carbon filament that would not make the inside of a light bulb turn dark. Later, in 1906, the General Electric Company patented a method of making tungsten filaments that were used in incandescent light bulbs.

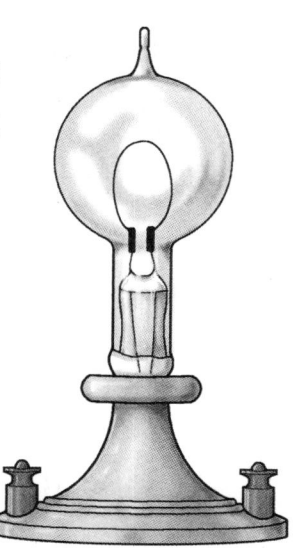

In 1809, an English scientist named **Humphry Davy** developed an electric battery to which he connected two wires with a charcoal strip between their ends. The charged carbon (charcoal) strip glowed, producing light. This was the first incandescent electric light.

In 1879, **Thomas Alva Edison** invented a carbon filament that burned for 40 hours. He later improved his light bulb until it could last for over 1200 hours using a filament derived from bamboo.

The first true light bulb was invented by **Henry Goebel,** a German watchmaker, in 1854. To create his light, Goebel used a filament of carbonized bamboo that he placed under a glass bulb.

GOBEL WATCH SHOP

Henry Goebel
Horologist

Edward Shepard invented an arc lamp in 1850. This electrical incandescent light used a charcoal filament.

In 1878, the English physicist **Sir Joseph Wilson Swan** invented an electric light using a filament made from carbonized paper. The light glowed for 13.5 hours.

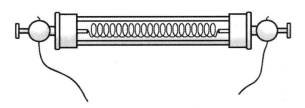

In 1829, **Warren de la Rue** put a platinum coil inside a tube and removed most of the air. He then passed an electric current through the coil, causing it to glow. His lamp design worked, but because platinum is so expensive, it was not practical for wide-spread use.

Fiddling With Filaments

Sketch the model light bulb.

Sketch the commercial light bulb.

Description:

Description:

Fiddling With Filaments

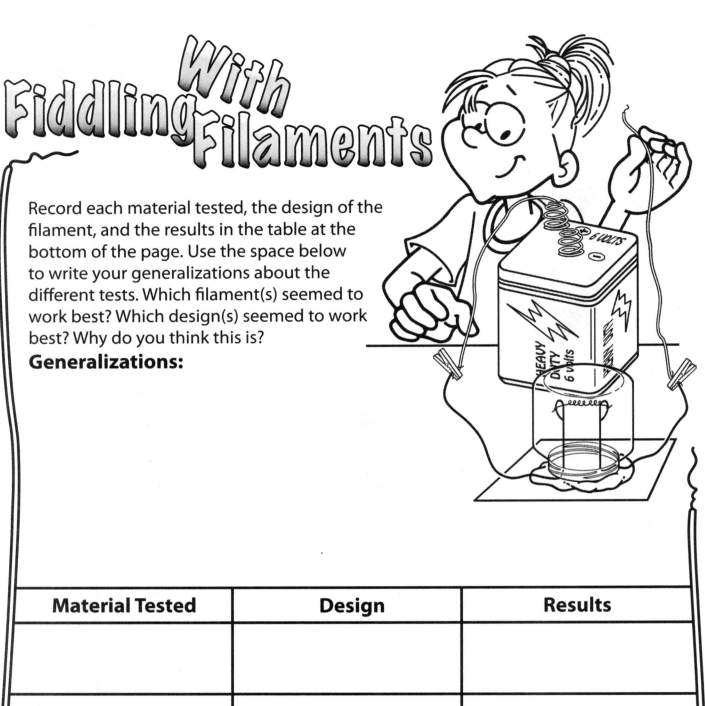

Record each material tested, the design of the filament, and the results in the table at the bottom of the page. Use the space below to write your generalizations about the different tests. Which filament(s) seemed to work best? Which design(s) seemed to work best? Why do you think this is?

Generalizations:

Material Tested	Design	Results

© 2011 AIMS Education Foundation

Fiddling With Filaments

Connecting Learning

1. How was your model light bulb similar to a commercially made bulb? ...different?

2. Which filament material created the brightest light? ...longest lasting light?

3. What problems, if any, did you encounter while trying to get the bulb to light?

4. What did you learn from this experience?

Fiddling With Filaments

Connecting Learning

5. What, if anything, surprised you about the materials that you tested?

6. Why was it necessary that the filament be a conductor?

7. In what other electrical devices have you seen filaments that glow? How are these devises like a light bulb? How are they different?

8. What are you wondering now?

Topic
Electrical conductors and insulators

Key Question
What materials will conduct electricity?

Learning Goal
Students will test a variety of materials to determine if they are conductors or insulators.

Guiding Documents
Project 2061 Benchmarks
- *Make safe electrical connections with various plugs, sockets, and terminals.*
- *Keep records of their investigations and observations.*

NRC Standards
- *Electricity in circuits can produce light, heat, sound, and magnetic effects. Electrical circuits require a complete loop through which an electrical current can pass.*
- *Plan and conduct a simple investigation.*
- *Employ simple equipment and tools to gather data and extend the senses.*

Science
Physical science
    electricity
        conductors
        insulators

Integrated Processes
Observing
Predicting
Comparing and contrasting
Drawing conclusions

Materials
For each group:
    wire with ends stripped, 15-25 cm
    D cell
    bulb
    tape
    materials to be tested (see student page)

For each student:
    student pages

Background Information
A direct electrical current is a steady flow of electrical charges through a medium called a *conductor*. In solid conductors (which include all metals), it is the negatively charged electrons that flow and make up the electrical current. Metals have some electrons that are not tightly bound to any single atom; they are free to move about from atom to atom. These electrons are called *conducting electrons*.

Positive charges do not flow in a solid conductor, since the positively-charged protons are bound within the nuclei of atoms. These atoms are locked in the grid-like structure of the solid material and are not free to move. Therefore, the current in a solid conductor is caused by the movement of negative electric charges (electrons).

In liquids that conduct electricity, the electrical charges that flow can be positive, negative, or both. The negative charges are provided by either free electrons or *negative ions* (atoms or molecules with extra electrons). The positive charges are provided by *positive ions* (atoms or molecules that are missing electrons).

Materials that do not normally conduct electricity are called *insulators*. Other materials that conduct electricity to a lesser degree than conductors, but more than insulators, are called *semiconductors*; these are of great importance in electronics. *It is important to note that at certain voltages and temperatures, all materials will conduct electricity to some degree.* Even air, which is normally an excellent insulator, will conduct electrical charges when the voltage is high enough; lightning illustrates this. The only perfect insulator is a vacuum.

Management
1. Students should work in groups of two to four.
2. Beforehand, make a sample circuit to test the conductivity of materials and show students.
3. Bulbs (item number 1962), wire (item number 1968), and wire strippers (item number 1970) are available from AIMS.

Procedure
Part One
1. Distribute materials to each group.
2. Show students how to build a circuit to test the conductivity of materials using the D cell, wire, and light bulb.

3. For the first five objects listed, have students predict whether or not the object will conduct electricity. Instruct them to place the object in the circuit and record the results.
4. Have students pick five additional objects to test, and repeat the process.
5. Discuss the results and have students write conclusions in the space provided. Make sure that students note that some objects, like the pencil, are both conductors and insulators, depending on what part of the object is placed in the test circuit.

Part Two
1. Using the first page for reference, have students list the conductors and insulators in the appropriate boxes on the second page.
2. Discuss common characteristics of the conductors. Have the students record these characteristics in the space provided.
3. Discuss common characteristics of the insulators. Have the students record these characteristics in the space provided.
4. Distribute the third page. In the appropriate areas of the Venn diagram, have the students write the names of the objects tested. Discuss the results.

Connecting Learning
1. How are all the conductors alike?
2. How are all the insulators alike?
3. What distinguishes a conductor from an insulator?
4. Are there any objects that are both conductors and insulators? [pencil] How is this possible?
5. What other things do you think might be conductors?
6. What other things might be insulators?
7. Why are many wires coated with plastic or some other material?
8. What are you wondering now?

Extensions
1. Test other objects to see if they are insulators or conductors.
2. Build a different circuit to test the conductivity of materials.
3. Build a circuit to test the conductivity of various liquids.

Curriculum Correlation
Health
Discuss the importance of insulators to health and safety. Identify some of the places insulators are used in the classroom.

Conductor or Insulator?

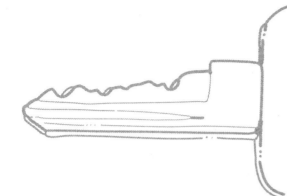

Key Question

What materials will conduct electricity?

Learning Goal

Students will:

test a variety of materials to determine if they are conductors or insulators.

                    © 2011 AIMS Education Foundation

Conductor or Insulator?

A *conductor* is any item that allows electrons to flow freely through it. The light bulb should light.

An *insulator* is any item that does not allow electrons to flow easily through it. The bulb will not light.

Tape one end of the wire to the bottom of the cell. Wrap the other end of wire around the metal side of the light bulb. Tape it securely in place.

Test each item. Record your findings in the table below.

Item	Prediction	Conductor	Insulator
paper clip			
tape			
pencil			
string			
ruler			

 © 2011 AIMS Education Foundation

Conductor or Insulator?

Conductors	Insulators

How are the conductors alike?

How are the insulators alike?

Conclusions:

© 2011 AIMS Education Foundation

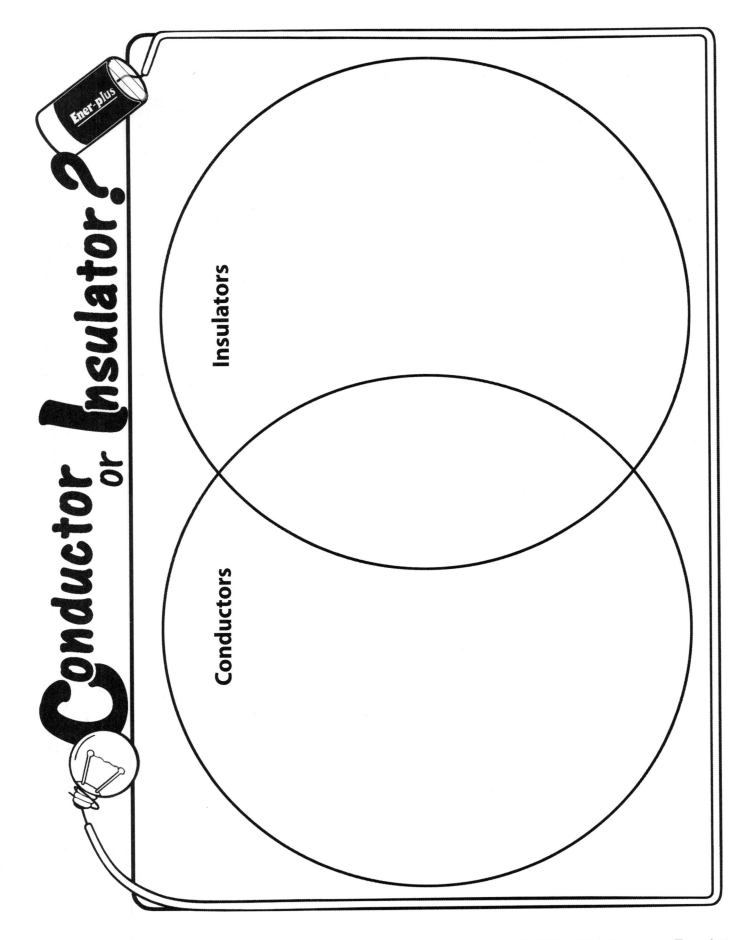

Conductor or Insulator?

Insulators

Conductors

94

© 2011 AIMS Education Foundation

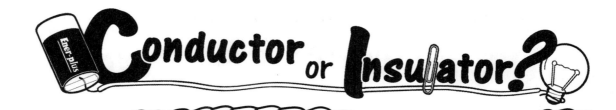

Connecting Learning

1. How are all the conductors alike?

2. How are all the insulators alike?

3. What distinguishes a conductor from an insulator?

4. Are there any objects that are both conductors and insulators? How is this possible?

5. What other things do you think might be conductors?

 © 2011 AIMS Education Foundation

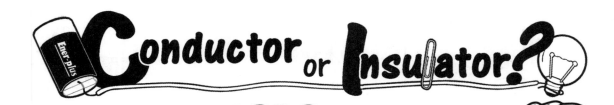

Conductor or Insulator?

Connecting Learning

6. What other things might be insulators?

7. Why are many wires coated with plastic or some other material?

8. What are you wondering now?

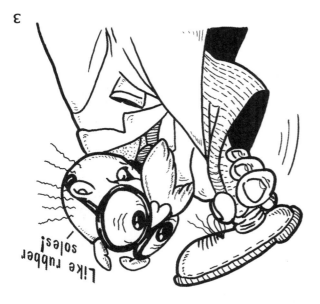

Like rubber soles!

Insulators are just the opposite. They do not let electricity move easily through them. Insulators help us use electricity safely. Some materials that are insulators are

- glass,
- plastic, and
- rubber.

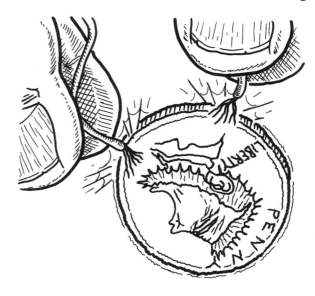

Conductors are materials that let electricity move easily through them. Most metals are good conductors of electricity. Copper is a conductor.

The cord on a lamp is made up of two parts. The rubber insulates us from the metal conductor inside. If you can see the wires inside, it is time to replace the cord.

Safety first, kids!

Conductors and Insulators

When you study electricity, you will hear the words *conductors* and *insulators*. These words describe how electricity moves through materials.

Make a Dimmer Switch

Topic
Electrical conductivity—semiconductors

Key Question
How does a dimmer switch work?

Learning Goal
Students will make a dimmer switch using a pencil lead.

Guiding Documents
Project 2061 Benchmarks
- *Make safe electrical connections with various plugs, sockets, and terminals.*
- *Keep records of their investigations and observations.*
- *Tables and graphs can show how values of one quantity are related to values of another.*
- *Organize data in simple tables and graphs and identify relationships they reveal.*

NRC Standards
- *Plan and conduct a simple investigation.*
- *Employ simple equipment and tools to gather data and extend the senses.*
- *Use mathematics in all aspects of scientific inquiry.*
- *Electricity in circuits can produce light, heat, sound, and magnetic effects. Electrical circuits require a complete loop through which an electrical current can pass.*

NCTM Standards 2000*
- *Collect data using observations, surveys, and experiments*
- *Represent data using tables and graphs such as line plots, bar graphs, and line graphs*

Math
Measurement
Graphing

Science
Physical science
    electricity
        dimmer switch

Integrated Processes
Observing
Comparing and contrasting
Drawing conclusions

Materials
For each group:
    2 D cells
    1.5-v bulb and holder
    15-cm wire with ends stripped
    two 8-cm wires with ends stripped
    tape
    metric ruler
    #2 pencil (see *Management 1*)
    scissors
    stapler

For each student:
    student pages

Background Information
Materials can be classified as to how well they conduct electricity. Those materials that readily conduct electricity are called *conductors,* while those that do not conduct electricity are called *insulators.* Between these two types of materials is a class of materials called *semiconductors.* Semiconductors conduct electricity, but not as well as conductors. Semiconductors are crucial to the electronics industry and are also used in household rheostats (dimmer switches). The ability of semiconductors to conduct electricity depends upon factors such as their length, thickness, and temperature. More current will travel through a short length of *semiconducting* material than through a long length. A dimmer switch simply changes the length of the path that the current takes through the semiconductor. As the length of the semiconductor changes, the brightness of the bulb changes. In this activity, the graphite in pencil lead is used as a semiconductor (although pencil leads are now made of graphite mixed with clay, they are still referred to as "leads.")

Management
1. Use #2 pencils or mechanical pencil lead of the same thickness (0.5 and 0.7 mm mechanical pencil leads are too small and fragile to work well). Both are available at office or art supply stores. Be sure leads are at least 10 cm long.
2. Prepare pencils beforehand. Using a utility knife, split pencils as shown on the activity sheet, removing about half of the wood so the lead can be touched easily. If desired, tape pencils or leads to flat surfaces before using to avoid breakage; be sure the test scale starts and ends within the untaped portion.

3. Beforehand, make a sample brightness indicator using a copy of the third student page. Cut out pieces and assemble in numerical order, with the shortest on top. Staple together as shown.

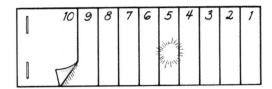

4. The brightness test works best with the classroom lights off.
5. Work in collaborative learning groups, with these roles:
   Student #1 holds battery connections firmly.
   Student #2 moves the wire ends on the pencil lead.
   Student #3 holds the brightness indicator over the bulb and makes the readings.
   Student #4 records all data.
6. Bulbs (item number 1962), bulb holders (item number 1958), insulated wire (item number 1968), wire strippers (item number 1970), and metric rulers (item number 1909) are available from AIMS.

Procedure
1. Discuss the *Key Question:* "How does a dimmer switch work?" Explain that this activity will help them understand how dimmer switches work.
2. Distribute materials to each group and have students build the test circuit pictured on the first student page.
3. Have each group make a brightness indicator (see *Management).*
4. Have students test the brightness of the bulb as the current goes through each length of pencil lead indicated and record results.
5. Discuss the results and have students write their conclusions in the space provided.
6. Have students construct a broken-line graph of their findings using the second student page.

Connecting Learning
1. Was there a difference in the brightness of the bulb as the wire was moved along the lead?
2. What might explain this difference? [different lengths of pencil lead for current to travel through]
3. In what ways is a real dimmer switch like the dimmer switch in this activity? [The length of semiconducting material that the current travels through varies as the switch is turned.]
4. In what ways is it different? [smaller, different materials used, etc.]
5. What are you wondering now?

Extensions
1. Take apart an old dimmer switch and examine the parts.
2. Use different thicknesses of pencil lead and see if there is a difference.

* Reprinted with permission from *Principles and Standards for School Mathematics,* 2000 by the National Council of Teachers of Mathematics. All rights reserved.

Make a Dimmer Switch

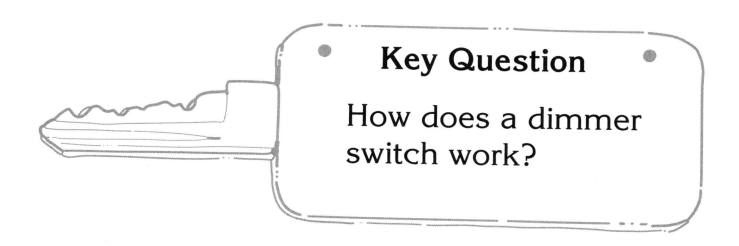

Key Question

How does a dimmer switch work?

Learning Goal

Students will:

will make a dimmer switch using
a pencil lead.

Make a Dimmer Switch

How does the distance current travels through a pencil lead affect the brightness of a bulb? Make the circuit and brightness tester shown below and find out!

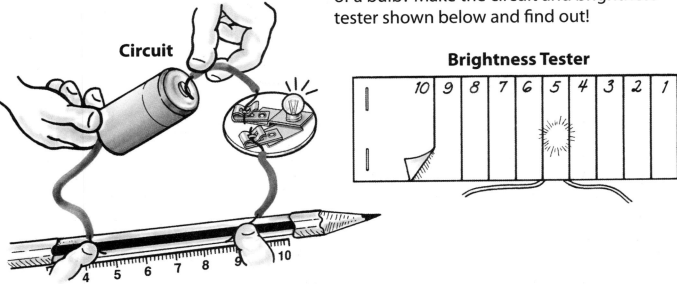

Circuit

Brightness Tester

Distance Current Travels Through Pencil Lead	Brightness of Bulb as Measured by Number of Sheets of Paper Bulb Shines Through									
	1	2	3	4	5	6	7	8	9	10
10 cm										
8 cm										
6 cm										
4 cm										
2 cm										

Conclusions:

Make a Dimmer Switch

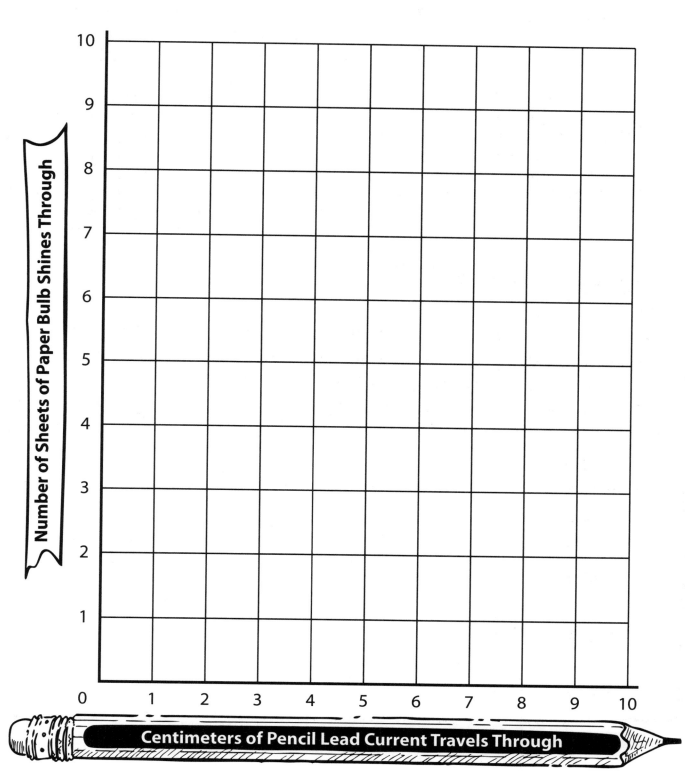

Number of Sheets of Paper Bulb Shines Through

Centimeters of Pencil Lead Current Travels Through

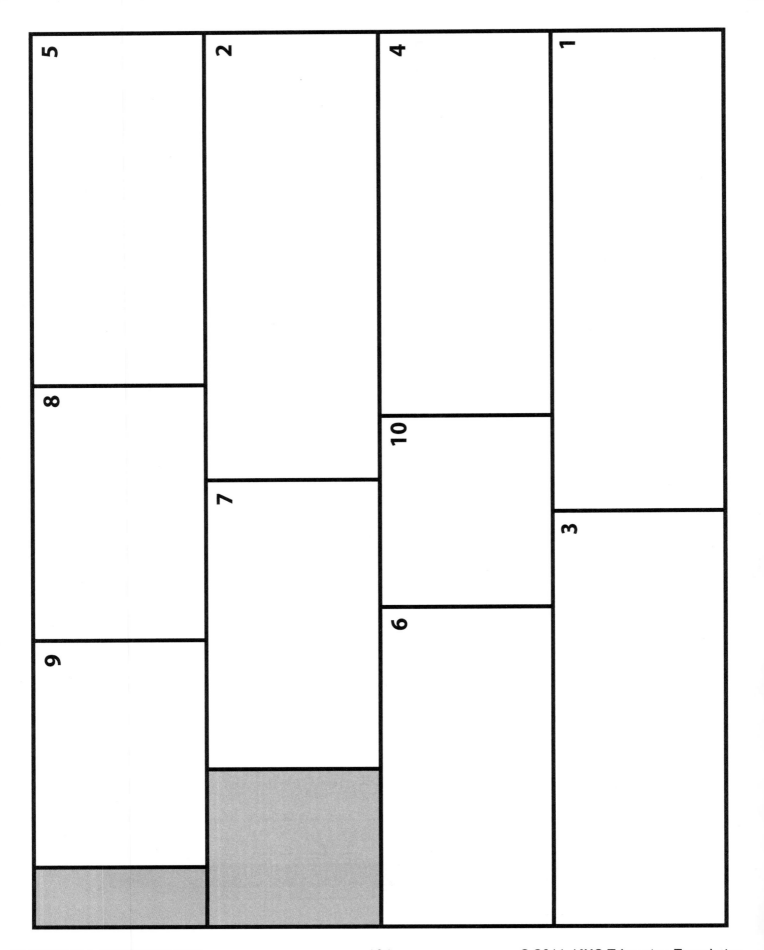

Make a Dimmer Switch

Connecting Learning

1. Was there a difference in the brightness of the bulb as the wire was moved along the lead?

2. What might explain this difference?

3. In what ways is a real dimmer switch like the dimmer switch in this activity?

4. In what ways is it different?

5. What are you wondering now?

 © 2011 AIMS Education Foundation

Make a Switch

Topic
Electrical switches and circuits

Key Questions
1. How can you turn the current on and off in an electrical circuit?
2. How can you turn a light on from two different parts of a room?

Learning Goals
Students will:
- build a simple switch to control the flow of electricity in a circuit, and
- build multiway switches.

Guiding Documents
Project 2061 Benchmark
- *Make safe electrical connections with various plugs, sockets, and terminals.*

NRC Standards
- *Plan and conduct a simple investigation.*
- *Employ simple equipment and tools to gather data and extend the senses.*
- *Electricity in circuits can produce light, heat, sound, and magnetic effects. Electrical circuits require a complete loop through which an electrical current can pass.*

Science
Physical science
electricity
circuits and switches

Integrated Processes
Observing
Comparing and contrasting
Drawing conclusions

Materials
Part One
For each group:
D cell
three 15-cm wires with ends stripped
two paper fasteners
1.5-v bulb and holder

paper clip
masking tape
3" x 5" index card
glue stick
hole punch
instruction page

Part Two
For each group:
materials from *Part One* plus:
two 10-cm wires with ends stripped
six more paper fasteners
two more paper clips
two more 3" x 5" index cards
two crayons, different colors
instruction page

Background Information
Most electrical devices have switches of one type or another, allowing the device to be turned on and off. An electric current will flow only if it has a complete path through which to travel. Switches are simple devices that complete or interrupt that path. When a switch is turned on (closed), it bridges a gap in the wiring, completing a path for electricity. When a switch is turned off (opened), it creates a gap in the circuit and stops the flow of electricity. Most electrical devices are controlled by a single-pole switch that works like the one built in *Part One*.

Some lights or other electrical devices are controlled by two or more switches. Those built in *Part Two* are multiway switches; they allow the device to be turned on or off from either switch.

Management
1. Students should work in groups of two or three.
2. *Part One* and *Part Two* can be done on the same day or on separate days.
3. Make sure the paper fasteners do not touch underneath the switches. If they do, they will create a short circuit and the switches will not be able to turn off.
4. Bulbs (item number 1962), bulb holders (item number 1960), wire (item number 1968), and wire strippers (item number 1970) are available from AIMS.

Procedure

Part One

1. Discuss the first *Key Question*: "How can you turn the current on and off in an electrical circuit?"
2. Distribute the materials and have each group build the circuit and switch pictured. Point out similar switches in the classroom.
3. Discuss the results, and have students record their observations and explanations.
4. Have them save their switches for use in other activities.

Part Two

1. Discuss the second *Key Question*: "How can you turn a light on from two different parts of a room?" Discuss multiway switches located either in the classroom or in students' homes. If your students live where there are no multiway switches, find some at school they can observe.
2. Distribute the additional materials. Have students build the switches and circuit as shown and follow the directions to operate the switches.
3. Have students write the explanation for how the multiway switches work. (They may need guidance.)

Connecting Learning

1. Why is it important to wrap the wire around the paper fasteners? [to make a good connection between the wire and the paper fastener]
2. What position does the paper clip have to be in for the bulb to light? [touching both paper fasteners]
3. Do you think all switches work the same way?
4. What is the advantage of having multiway switches hooked up to a light? [They can be turned off and on from multiple locations.]
5. Explain how a multiway switch works. [It allows you to turn the light off or on from two different places. When the light is off, moving either switch to the opposite position will cause the light to go on, and vice versa.]
6. What are some ways that switches are used in the classroom?
7. Why are switches important?
8. What are you wondering now?

Extensions

1. Make a switch using other materials.
2. Make diagrams of all the possible switch positions (and whether or not they light the bulb) for the multiway switch circuit.
3. Using a box, make a model of a room with two doors. Wire the light using the circuit made for *Part Two* so that it can be turned on or off from either door.

Home Links

1. Have students count the number of wall and appliance switches they have at home. How many are single pole? How many are multiway?
2. Challenge students to explain multiway switches to members of their families. Share reactions to the explanations.

Make a Switch

Key Questions

1. How can you turn the current on and off in an electrical circuit?

2. How can you turn a light on from two different parts of a room?

Learning Goals

Students will:

- build a simple switch to control the flow of electricity in a circuit, and

- build multiway switches.

 © 2011 AIMS Education Foundation

Make a Switch

How can you make an electric switch?

You will need these things:
- 3" x 5" index card
- three 15-cm pieces of insulated wire
- two paper fasteners
- 1.5-volt bulb and holder
- one D cell
- paper clip
- masking tape
- glue stick
- hole punch

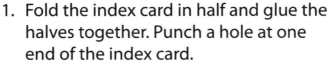

1. Fold the index card in half and glue the halves together. Punch a hole at one end of the index card.
2. Put a paper fastener through one end of the paper clip and then through the hole. Fasten the paper clip to the index card.
3. Punch a second hole in the index card close enough for the paper clip to touch. Put the other paper fastener through this hole and fasten it to the index card.
4. Tape the ends of the paper fasteners under the index cards so they do not touch each other.
5. Connect the wires as shown, winding them around the paper fasteners once or twice.
6. Close the switch by pressing the paper clip on the paper fastener.

What happens?

Explain how your switch works.

ELECTRICAL CONNECTIONS

© 2011 AIMS Education Foundation

Make a Switch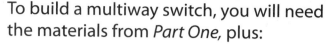

How can you turn a light on from two different parts of a room?

To build a multiway switch, you will need the materials from *Part One*, plus:

> two 3" x 5" index cards
> six paper fasteners
> two 10-cm pieces of insulated wire
> two paper clips
> two crayons, different colors

1. Build two additional switches like the ones you made in *Part One*. This time, punch a third hole in each index card and insert a paper fastener so that the paper clip can touch both paper fasteners.

2. Set up the circuit as shown here. Tape the ends of the paper fasteners under the index cards so they do not touch each other.

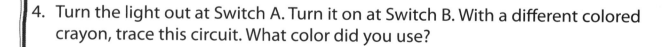

3. Try the switch in both positions until you make the bulb light. Using a crayon on this sheet, trace the path of the electric current. What color did you use?

4. Turn the light out at Switch A. Turn it on at Switch B. With a different colored crayon, trace this circuit. What color did you use?

5. Explain how your multiway switch works.

 © 2011 AIMS Education Foundation

Make a Switch

Connecting Learning

1. Why is it important to wrap the wire around the paper fasteners?

2. What position does the paper clip have to be in for the bulb to light?

3. Do you think all switches work the same way? Explain.

4. What is the advantage of having multiway switches hooked up to a light?

5. Explain how a multiway switch works.

Make a Switch

Connecting Learning

6. What are some ways that switches are used in the classroom?

7. Why are switches important?

8. What are you wondering now?

 © 2011 AIMS Education Foundation

Circuit Breakers

Topic
Circuit breakers

Key Question
How does a circuit breaker prevent a circuit from overheating?

Learning Goal
Students will build a circuit breaker and learn its function as part of a circuit.

Guiding Documents
Project 2061 Benchmarks
- *Make safe electrical connections with various plugs, sockets, and terminals.*
- *Many systems contain feedback methods that serve to keep changes within specified limits.*

NRC Standards
- *Employ simple equipment and tools to gather data and extend the senses.*
- *Electricity in circuits can produce light, heat, sound, and magnetic effects. Electrical circuits require a complete loop through which an electrical current can pass.*

Science
Physical science
    electricity

Integrated Processes
Observing
Drawing conclusions
Generalizing
Applying

Materials
For each group:
    two or three balloons
    one paper clip switch (see *Management 4*)
    two or three D cells
    aluminum foil wires (see *Management 5*)
    insulated wire (see *Management 5*)
    three or four strands of steel wool, 3-5 cm
    tape
    1.5-v bulb and holder

For each student:
    Circuit Breakers rubber band book
    #19 rubber band
    student page

Background Information
A switch is one device that can complete or interrupt a circuit. Circuit breakers and fuses are other devices that do the same thing; they act as a *weak link* in a circuit because they are designed to stop the flow of electricity if the circuit becomes overloaded and begins to get too hot. These devices are crucial in helping prevent electrical fires.

Electricity flowing through a circuit will always generate some heat. The amount of heat depends on the resistance of the circuit and the amount of current present. Electrical circuits are designed to carry certain amounts of electricity without getting dangerously hot. When the amount of current in a circuit exceeds this level, fires can result. To prevent this from happening, circuit breakers and/or fuses are placed in electrical circuits; they are designed to interrupt the circuit when current exceeds safe levels.

Circuit breakers work in several different ways. The most common type uses an electromagnetic mechanism to interrupt the circuit when too much current is present. Another type uses a heat sensitive device similar to a thermostat to trigger the circuit interruption.

The circuit breaker in this activity doesn't work like a normal circuit breaker, but it does model how it breaks the circuit and interrupts the flow of electricity when the wires in the circuit get too hot. In this model, the strands of steel wool taped to the balloon determine how much current can pass through the circuit before the circuit breaks. These thin strands have a fairly high resistance to the flow of electricity. When a small amount of current is flowing through the circuit, as is the case when the light bulb is part of the circuit, these strands don't overheat because the resistance in the bulb filament is much higher than the resistance in the strands of steel wool. When the foil strip bypassing the bulb is added to the circuit, it creates a short circuit—a path for the electricity to flow through with much less resistance than when it was forced to go through the light bulb. This extra current quickly heats up the steel wool strands and they melt the balloon, causing it to pop. This literally breaks the circuit, interrupting the flow of electricity.

Management
1. Students should work in groups of three or four.
2. You should try this activity yourself before doing it with students. This experience will better help you present it to your students.

3. As in any electric circuit, loose connections may cause problems. All of the circuit components must be well connected if this investigation is to work properly.
4. Students should use the switch they made in *Part One* of the activity *Make a Switch*. The switch requires two paper fasteners, a paper clip, and a 3" x 5" index card.
5. Students need both aluminum foil wires and insulated wires for this activity. To make aluminum foil wires, cover a piece of foil with masking tape and cut it into strips about 2 cm wide. Give each group four foil wires—two long (20-30 cm) and two short (10-15 cm). Cut the insulated wire into 12-cm lengths and strip the ends. Each group needs two pieces of insulated wire.
6. Insulated wire (item number 1968), bulbs (item number 1962), bulb holders (item number 1958), and wire strippers (item number 1970) are available from AIMS.

Procedure
1. Ask students if they know what a circuit breaker is and what is does. Listen to responses.
2. Distribute the rubber band book and #19 rubber bands to students. Read the book together as a class and discuss the *Key Question*: "How does a circuit breaker keep a circuit from overheating?" [It interrupts, or breaks, the circuit when too much current is flowing through it.]
3. Distribute the student page and explain the procedure for making the circuit breakers.
4. Make sure students have the switch in the open (off) position when setting up the circuit.
5. Once the circuits are set up, have students close the switch for a few seconds and observe what happens. (Hopefully the light will come on and the balloon will not pop.)
6. Have students open the switch and add the foil strip as shown in the fourth diagram. This creates a short circuit that bypasses the higher-resistance bulb filament and allows a large amount of current to flow through the circuit.
7. After adding the strip, have students close the switch. The extra current caused by this short circuit quickly heats the thin steel wool strands because they have more resistance than the foil. The heat should be enough to melt the rubber of the balloon and cause it to pop. When the balloon pops, the circuit is broken and electricity can no longer flow through it.
8. Discuss the results.

Connecting Learning
1. Why didn't the balloon pop when the circuit was closed and the light bulb lit up? [The high resistance of the bulb filament prevented too much current from flowing through the circuit. This kept the strands of steel wool from getting hot enough to pop the balloon.]
2. Why did the balloon pop when the foil strip bypassing the bulb was added? [The foil strip has much less resistance to the flow of electricity than the bulb filament. The strip created a short circuit that bypassed the bulb and allowed much more current to flow through the circuit. This extra current caused the strands of steel wool, which have higher resistance than the foil, to heat up enough to pop the balloon.]
3. Why does the circuit breaker in your home turn off the current to a circuit when you operate too many appliances on that circuit? [When too many appliances are running simultaneously on a single circuit, they draw more electric current than the circuit was designed to carry. This extra current heats up the wires in the circuit enough that they could start a fire if the circuit were not interrupted by the circuit breaker.]
4. Why is it dangerous to use electrical appliances that have worn or frayed cords? [The insulation on the cords keeps the two embedded wires from touching. If they are worn enough so that the embedded wires touch, a short circuit occurs and there is almost no resistance to the current flowing in the circuit. The wires very quickly get hot enough to start a fire unless a circuit breaker interrupts the circuit first.]
5. What are you wondering now?

Extensions
1. Hook your balloon circuit breaker to a circuit containing three lights in series. Does it pop with the same number of cells?
2. Hook your balloon circuit breaker to a circuit containing three lights in parallel. What difference does this make?

*We would like to give special thanks to **Ron Marson** from **Tops Learning Systems** for permission to adapt this lesson from the Tops activity, **Big Bang**.*

© 2011 AIMS Education Foundation

Circuit Breakers

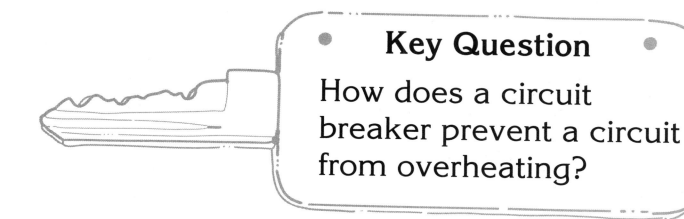

Key Question

How does a circuit breaker prevent a circuit from overheating?

Learning Goal

build a circuit breaker and learn its function as part of a circuit.

          © 2011 AIMS Education Foundation

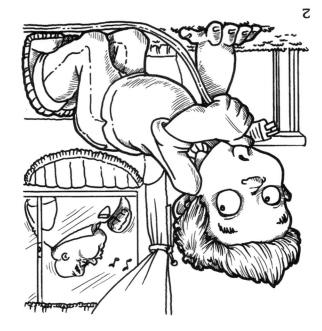

When a circuit is tripped, the circuit breaker has to be reset for electricity to flow again. If a circuit breaker keeps going off, that means there are too many things happening on the same circuit.

Have you ever plugged something in or turned something on and suddenly—POP—the power goes out? Maybe your dad went outdoors to the side of the house and then suddenly, the power was back on.

Circuit breakers help keep us safe by preventing fires. They also help us know when we are trying to put too many things on the same circuit.

Circuit Breakers

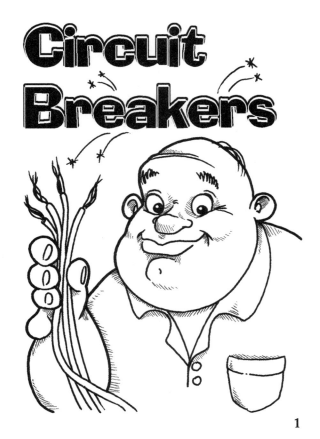

© 2011 AIMS Education Foundation

That's where circuit breakers come in. These "weak links" break the circuit when there is too much current. They keep the circuit from getting too hot and help prevent electrical fires.

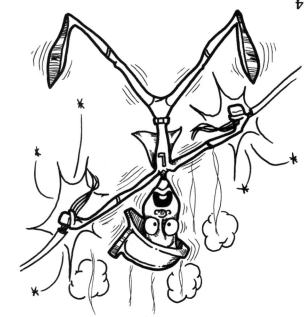

Electricity flows through circuits. A circuit is only designed to handle a certain amount of electric current. If too much current is present, the circuit gets too hot. The heat can start an electrical fire.

Houses, apartments, and other buildings have many different circuits to provide electricity. Each circuit has a breaker. These breakers are all together in a panel.

When something like this happens, a circuit breaker has been tripped, or set off. So, what is a circuit breaker? Think of it like a weak link.

© 2011 AIMS Education Foundation

Circuit Breakers

You need:
Balloon
Steel wool
Transparent tape
Paper clip switch
Bulb and holder
Foil wires
Insulated wires
Two D cells
Heavy duty rubber band

1 Blow up and tie your balloon. Tape three strands of steel wool to it as shown.

2 Tape two aluminum foil wires to the ends of the steel wool, foil side up.

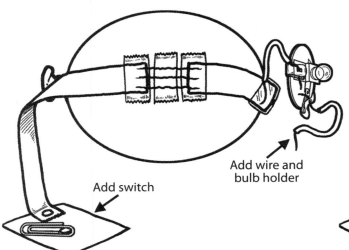

Add wire and bulb holder

Add switch

3 Add the insulated wire and bulb holder to one of the aluminum foil wires. Add the switch to the other foil wire.

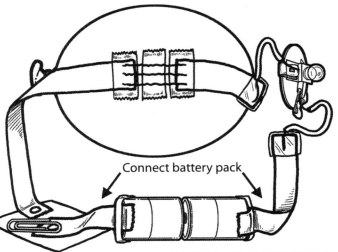

Connect battery pack

4 With the switch open, connect the light and the switch to the battery pack as shown.

© 2011 AIMS Education Foundation

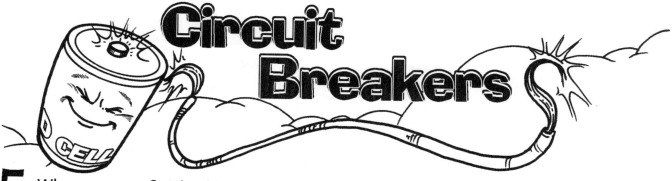

Circuit Breakers

5 When you are finished building the circuit, close the switch and observe what happens. Describe what you observed. Why did this happen?

6 Open the switch. Add an additional piece of foil wire to the circuit by taping it between the two foil wires as shown. Be sure that the foil sides are touching.

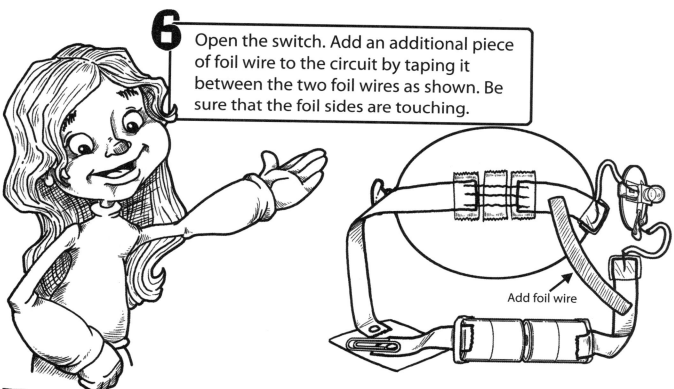

Add foil wire

7 Close the switch and observe what happens. Describe what you observed. Why did this happen?

© 2011 AIMS Education Foundation

Circuit Breakers

Connecting Learning

1. Why didn't the balloon pop when the circuit was closed and the light bulb lit up?

2. Why did the balloon pop when the foil strip bypassing the bulb was added?

3. Why does the circuit breaker in your home turn off the current to a circuit when you operate too many appliances on that circuit?

4. Why is it dangerous to use electrical appliances that have worn or frayed cords?

5. What are you wondering now?

 © 2011 AIMS Education Foundation

Electric Circuits

Topic
Series and parallel circuits

Key Question
How does the flow of electricity in a series circuit differ from the flow in a parallel circuit?

Learning Goals
Students will:
- build series and parallel circuits, and
- compare the two types of circuits.

Guiding Documents
Project 2061 Benchmarks
- *Make safe electrical connections with various plugs, sockets, and terminals.*
- *Make sketches to aid in explaining procedures or ideas.*

NRC Standards
- *Employ simple equipment and tools to gather data and extend the senses.*
- *Use data to construct a reasonable explanation.*
- *Electricity in circuits can produce light, heat, sound, and magnetic effects. Electrical circuits require a complete loop through which an electrical current can pass.*

Science
Physical science
    electricity
        circuits

Integrated Processes
Observing
Predicting
Drawing conclusions

Materials
For each group:
    two D cells
    three small bulbs and holders
    10 pieces of wire, 20-30 cm
    wire stripper, if needed (see *Management 3*)
    rubber band, heavy duty

For each student:
    student pages

Background Information
There are two basic types of electric circuits, *series* and *parallel*. In a series circuit, there is only one path for the current, and a break in the circuit stops the current. In a parallel circuit, there are multiple pathways or branches. If there is a break in any branch, the current will still go through the other branches. Only if all the branches have breaks will the current stop.

An added factor in any electric circuit is the resistance involved. Electrical resistance is anything that hinders the flow of electricity. The amount of resistance in a conductor depends on the conductivity of the material, its length, thickness, and temperature. Electrical devices such as motors, transistors, and lights add resistance to a circuit. An electric bulb, for example, has much more resistance than the wires in a circuit since its filament is long, thin, and made of a material with high resistance. In circuits, the amount of current varies with the resistance. Circuits with less resistance allow more electricity to flow, while circuits with more resistance restrict the amount of current.

If three bulbs are connected in series, the current goes through each bulb in turn, and the resistance of each bulb is added to the total resistance of the circuit. Less current goes through the circuit and the bulbs glow less brightly than a single bulb would. If a bulb is removed, the path is broken and the current stops.

If the three bulbs are connected in parallel, the current has multiple paths, and the resistance in the circuit is reduced. Since there is less resistance, more electricity flows and each bulb glows as brightly as a single bulb. If a bulb is removed, the others stay lit since the current goes through the other branches of the circuit.

Management
1. Students should work in groups of three or four.
2. Bulbs (item number 1962), bulb holders (item number 1958), wire (item number 1968), and wire strippers (item number 1970) are available from AIMS.
3. The ends of the wires will need to be stripped prior to building the circuits.

Procedure

Part One

1. Distribute the materials to each group.
2. Have each group build the series circuit pictured and predict what will happen when one of the bulbs is removed. Have students remove a bulb and record the results.
3. Have students build the parallel circuit pictured and predict what will happen when a bulb is removed. Have them test their predictions and record results.
4. Have some groups replace the bulb in the parallel circuit while others rebuild the series circuit.
5. Direct students to compare the brightness of the bulbs in the two circuits. Have them record their observations on the activity sheet.
6. Discuss the results and record conclusions.

Part Two

1. Discuss the schematic diagram and have students build the circuit pictured.
2. Have students build circuits of their own and then make schematic diagrams.
3. Invite students to exchange diagrams and build the circuits pictured.

Connecting Learning

1. Why did the other bulbs in the series circuit go out when one bulb was removed? [In a series circuit, there is only one path for the current, and removing the bulb breaks that path and stops the current.]
2. Why did the other bulbs in the parallel circuit stay lit when one bulb was removed? [In a parallel circuit, there are multiple pathways for the current, and breaking one path doesn't keep current from going through the other paths.]
3. Why are the bulbs in the parallel circuit brighter than the bulbs in the series circuit? [There are more paths for the current and less resistance in the parallel circuit.]
4. What problems might you have when lights (such as Christmas tree lights) are wired in series? [When one bulb burns out, it breaks the circuit and all the lights go off. It is often difficult to find the defective bulb, and each bulb in the series must be tested individually.]
5. What kind of circuit is most common in our homes? [parallel] Why?
6. What are you wondering now?

Extensions

1. Try more than three bulbs in the circuits.
2. Add switches or buzzers to your circuits.
3. Try different numbers of cells in the circuits.
4. Use two identical (new) cells and put one in each circuit. Leave the circuits on until both cells are dead. Compare the difference in how long they lasted.

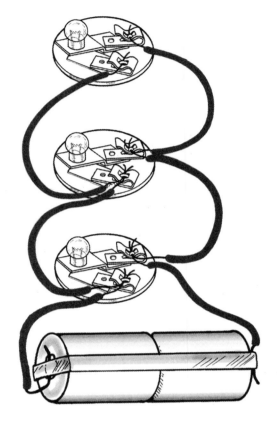

 © 2011 AIMS Education Foundation

Electric Circuits

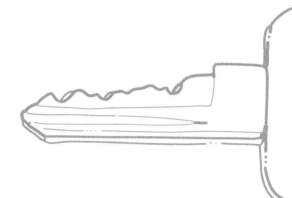

Key Question

How does the flow of electricity in a series circuit differ from the flow in a parallel circuit?

Learning Goals

Students will:

- build series and parallel circuits, and

- compare the two types of circuits.

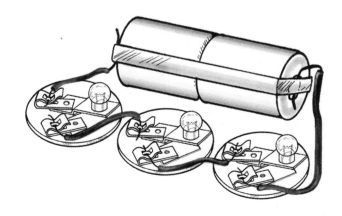

Electric Circuits

How does the flow of electricity in a series circuit differ from the flow of electricity in a parallel circuit?

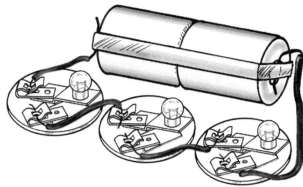

Series

1. Build a series circuit like this.

2. What happens when you remove a bulb?

Prediction

Results

3. Build a parallel circuit like this.

4. What happens when you remove a bulb?

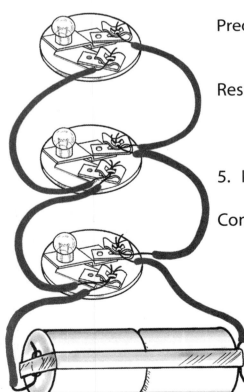

Prediction

Results

5. In which kind of circuit did the bulbs glow more brightly?

Conclusions

Parallel

Electric Circuits

Here is a schematic diagram of an electric circuit. Electricians use diagrams like this when they put electric circuits into houses and other buildings.

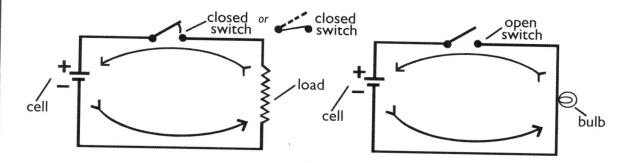

1. Build a circuit using this diagram as a plan. Use a dry cell (battery) for your power supply and a bulb for your load.

   Notice that there is a switch. When the switch is open, the circuit is broken. If you do not have a switch for your circuit, what else can you do to break the circuit and turn off your light?

2. Now make another circuit. After you have built it, make a diagram of it like the one above. See if a friend can follow your diagram and build your circuit.

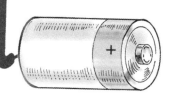

127 © 2011 AIMS Education Foundation

Electric Circuits

Connecting Learning

1. Why did the other bulbs in the series circuit go out when one bulb was removed?

2. Why did the other bulbs in the parallel circuit stay lit when one bulb was removed?

3. Why are the bulbs in the parallel circuit brighter than the bulbs in the series circuit?

4. What problems might you have when lights (such as Christmas tree lights) are wired in series?

5. What kind of circuits is most common in our homes? Why?

6. What are you wondering now?

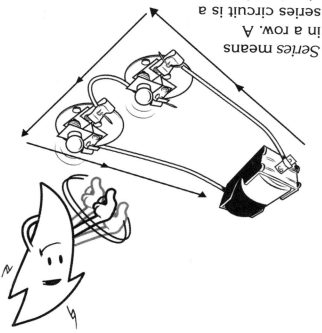

Series means in a row. A series circuit is a circuit with only one path for electricity to flow through. The components are all in a row, one after the other. This picture shows a series circuit.

Some miniature tree lights are wired in series. There is only one path for the electrical current. If there is a break in a series circuit at any point, the whole circuit stops working.

That means that if any one of the light bulbs burns out or is removed, no bulbs will light.

SERIES CIRCUITS

Warning! It is very easy to keep adding lights in a parallel circuit. This means that you can overload the circuit. If you use too much current, the circuit is not safe.

Parallel means side by side. A parallel circuit is a circuit with at least two separate paths for the electricity to flow through. This picture shows a parallel circuit.

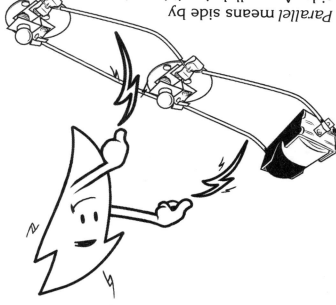

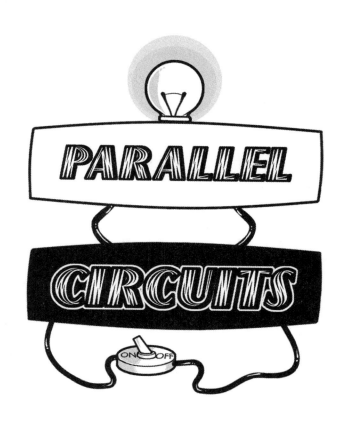

THE END

PARALLEL CIRCUITS

ELECTRICAL CONNECTIONS

© 2011 AIMS Education Foundation

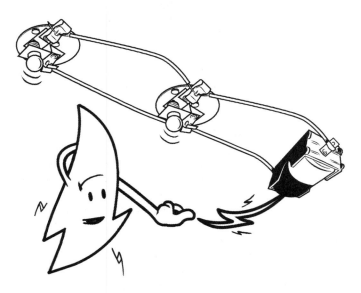

In a parallel circuit like this, both bulbs glow at full brightness. They are both getting full power from the battery.

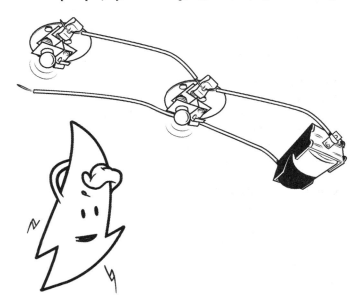

In a parallel circuit, if one path is broken (open), the current will not stop. It will still flow through the unbroken (closed) paths. Only when all paths are broken will the current stop.

You want miniature tree lights that are on a parallel circuit. If one light burns out, the others will keep burning.

Notice that there is a path for electricity to flow through to both bulbs. The electricity starts at the power source (battery). Then it goes through each separate path. It lights the bulbs and goes back to the source.

ELECTRICAL CONNECTIONS

© 2011 AIMS Education Foundation

SHORT CUTS

Topic
Electrical circuits

Key Question
How will adding a switch to one of the branches of a parallel circuit affect the flow of electricity?

Learning Goals
Students will:
- build several different parallel circuits, each with a switch; and
- discover the effect on each circuit when the switch is opened and closed.

Guiding Documents
Project 2061 Benchmark
- *Make safe electrical connections with various plugs, sockets, and terminals.*

NRC Standards
- *Ask a question about objects and events in the environment.*
- *Employ simple equipment and tools to gather data and extend the senses.*
- *Use data to construct a reasonable explanation.*
- *Electricity in circuits can produce light, heat, sound, and magnetic effects. Electrical circuits require a complete loop through which an electrical current can pass.*

Science
Physical science
  electricity
    circuits
    switches

Makes sense to me!

Integrated Processes
Observing
Predicting
Comparing and contrasting
Drawing conclusions

Materials
For each group:
  two D cells
  two bulbs and holders
  one switch (see *Management 3*)
  six 15-25 cm pieces of wire

For each student:
  student pages

Background Information
Whenever a current flows through a circuit, it meets with resistance. The amount of resistance in a circuit is determined by one or more of these factors: the material of the wires, their length and thickness, their temperature, the type and number of electrical devices involved (bulbs, resistors, capacitors, etc.), and the type of circuit (series or parallel). In a *series circuit,* every device placed in the circuit adds resistance to the small amount present in the circuit's wires. In a *parallel circuit,* more current will flow through the branch(es) with less resistance and less current will go through the branch(es) with greater resistance.

In the parallel circuit built in *Part One,* the switch placed in one branch changes the way that current flows; when the switch is on (closed), it provides a path with less resistance than the other two branches containing bulbs (which have a high resistance). Most of the current goes through the low resistance branch and very little goes through the two branches with the high resistance bulbs (not enough current to cause them to light). When the switch is turned off (opened), current can no longer go through that branch; it goes through the branches with lights, and the bulbs glow. The lights are turned off by closing the switch and turned on by opening the switch.

In the first circuit in *Part Two,* the same thing happens. Even though the switch is in a different branch in this circuit, it still provides the path of least resistance when closed. It is important to note that current is flowing through both of these circuits when the switches are closed, even though the bulbs are not glowing.

In the second circuit in *Part Two,* the switch is in the same branch as one of the bulbs. In this circuit, the switch will turn the bulb in its branch on and off, while the bulb in the other branch will always be on.

In the third circuit in *Part Two,* the switch is placed between the battery and the branches of the circuit. In this circuit, the bulbs glow when the switch is closed and stop glowing when it is opened. The switch is wired in series. It is not presenting an alternate path for the current; it simply allows current to go through the circuit when it is closed and prevents current from flowing when it is open.

Electricians call an unwanted flow of electricity in a circuit a *short.* A short could also be called an *easy,* since each is an unintended path of least resistance (which sometimes is a longer path) taken by the current.

    © 2011 AIMS Education Foundation

The closed switches in the circuit in *Part One* and the first one in *Part Two* are *shorts,* since they provide an easy path for the current and divert most of it from the higher resistance bulbs.

Management
1. Students should work in groups of three or four.
2. Bulbs (item number 1962), bulb holders (item number 1958), wire (item number 1968), and wire strippers (item number 1970) are available from AIMS.
3. Students should use the switch they made in *Part One* of the activity *Make a Switch.* The switch requires two paper fasteners, a paper clip, and a 3" x 5" index card.

Procedure
Part One
1. Discuss the *Key Question*: "How will adding a switch to one of the branches of a parallel circuit affect the flow of electricity?"
2. Have students look at the circuit diagram and then read the four possible outcomes. Let each group guess which one of the outcomes is correct.
3. Have each group build the circuit and test it with the switch in both the open and closed positions. After finding the results, tell students to disconnect the cell so that it doesn't drain. (When the switch is closed and the lights are off, the cells are being quickly drained by the short circuit.)
4. Discuss the results, and have students write their conclusions in the space provided.

Part Two
1. Ask the students how the location of the switch affects the flow of electricity.
2. Have students look at each circuit and predict whether the bulbs will light when the switch is on (closed). Tell students to write their predictions and reasoning.
3. Direct each group to build and test the three circuits pictured, recording the results.
4. Discuss the results as a class, and have students write conclusions.

Connecting Learning
1. Why didn't the bulbs in the first two circuits light when the switch was closed? [The switch has less resistance than the bulbs and provides an easier path for the current, diverting most of it from the bulbs.]
2. Why did the bulbs in the first two circuits light when the switch was open? [The *easy* path was broken, forcing the electricity to go through the bulbs.]
3. What is a *short*? [a path that creates an unwanted flow of electricity in a circuit]
4. What are you wondering now?

Extensions
1. Build other circuits with more than one switch.
2. Build a parallel circuit with bulbs of different voltage.

SHORT CUTS

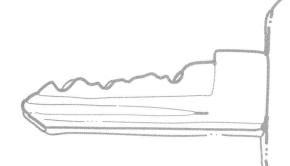

• Key Question

How will adding a switch to one of the branches of a parallel circuit affect the flow of electricity?

Learning Goals

Students will:

- build several different parallel circuits, each with a switch; and

- discover the effect on each circuit when the switch is opened and closed.

© 2011 AIMS Education Foundation

Part One

How will electricity flow in the circuit shown below?

Look at the diagram below and guess what will happen.

A. The bulbs will not light at all.
B. The bulbs will light when the switch is on (closed).
C. The bulbs will light when the switch is off (open).
D. Only one bulb will light.

Build the parallel circuit shown below.

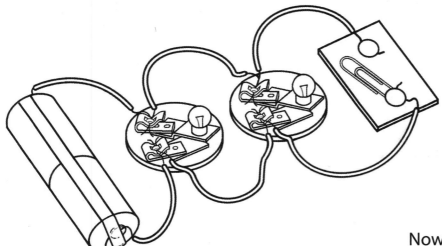

Now turn the switch on and off.

What happened?

How can you explain the results?

ELECTRICAL CONNECTIONS   136   © 2011 AIMS Education Foundation

How does the location of the switch affect the flow of electricity?

Build these circuits. Which bulbs will light when the switch is on?

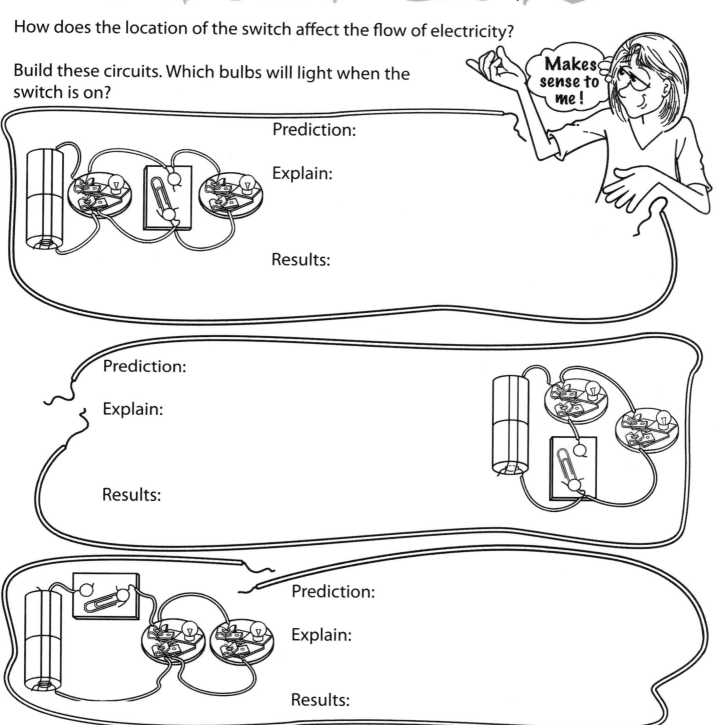

Makes sense to me!

Prediction:

Explain:

Results:

Prediction:

Explain:

Results:

Prediction:

Explain:

Results:

How can you explain the results?

SHORT CUTS

Connecting Learning

1. Why didn't the bulbs in the first two circuits light when the switch was closed?

2. Why did the bulbs in the first two circuits light when the switch was open?

3. What is a *short*?

4. What are you wondering now?

Topic
Electrical circuits—Morse code

Key Question
How can you build a device that will transmit messages using Morse code?

Learning Goals
Students will:
• build a telegraph, and
• send messages using Morse code.

Guiding Documents
Project 2061 Benchmarks
• *Make safe electrical connections with various plugs, sockets, and terminals.*
• *Communication involves coding and decoding information. In any language, both the sender and receiver have to know the same code, which means that that secret codes can be used to keep communication private.*

NRC Standard
• *Electricity in circuits can produce light, heat, sound, and magnetic effects. Electrical circuits require a complete loop through which an electrical current can pass.*

Science
Physical science
   electricity
      circuits

Integrated Processes
Observing
Comparing and contrasting
Communicating

Materials
For each group:
   D cell
   bulb and holder
   10-15 cm wires
   switch (see *Management 3*)
   tape

For each student:
   student page
   Samuel Morse rubber band book

Background Information
See rubber band book on Samuel Morse.

Management
1. This lesson works best with groups of two.
2. Use the rubber band book about Samuel Morse to introduce this lesson.
3. This lesson is designed to follow the lessons on circuits and switches. The students should be able to build a simple circuit with a switch (from the activity *Make a Switch)* and bulb to act as a telegraph. If not, you may want to have a sample circuit built ahead of time to show them.
4. Bulbs (item number 1962), bulb holders (item number 1958), and wire (item number 1968) are available from AIMS.

Procedure
1. Review the rubber band book about Samuel Morse and discuss how the Morse code can be used to transmit messages using short and long flashes of light (dots and dashes).
2. Discuss the *Key Question:* "How can you build a device that will transmit messages by code?"
3. Challenge students to build a circuit that will act as a telegraph and enable them to send messages to each other in Morse code.
4. Distribute the materials and student page, and have each group build a telegraph. Let the students use the student page to send each other messages.

Connecting Learning
1. How does your telegraph work?
2. How is the telegraph you built different from real telegraphs?
3. Why aren't telegraphs used widely today?
4. What devices have replaced the telegraph for communicating over long distances?
5. What are you wondering now?

Extensions
1. Investigate other coding systems.
2. Encourage students to devise their own codes.
3. Have students build telegraphs that use a buzzer instead of a bulb.
4. Have students research and build telegraphs that are more like real telegraphs.

Curriculum Correlation
Social Studies
Research other inventions that came on the scene about the same time as the telegraph. Study the history of the *Pony Express* and how the telegraph made it obsolete.

PUT YOUR NAME IN LIGHTS

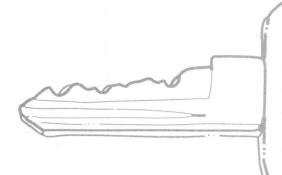

Key Question

How can you build a device that will transmit messages using Morse code?

Learning Goals

Students will:

- build a telegraph, and

- send messages using Morse code.

Samuel F.B. Morse

Samuel Morse was born on April 27, 1791 in Massachusetts. His interest in art plus his hard work led to success both as an artist and also an art teacher.

While sailing home from Europe in 1832, Morse learned that electricity could be sent instantly over any length of wire. This was the beginning of his quest to invent the telegraph.

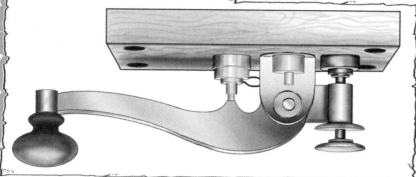

Morse tried one dramatic demonstration by laying wire under water. Crowds came to see the telegraph work. Unfortunately, a ship's anchor pulled up the wire and cut it. The disappointed crowd left, calling the whole thing a hoax.

Finally, with a grant of money from Congress, Morse succeeded. In 1844, Morse strung a wire from the Supreme Court Building in Washington, D.C. to Baltimore, Maryland. He sent the now famous message, "What hath God wrought?" Morse won great fame and wealth from his invention. He died in 1872.

© 2011 AIMS Education Foundation

PUT YOUR NAME IN LIGHTS

International Morse Code

-- --- .-. ... .   -.-. --- -.. .

A dot is a short flash of light. A dash is three times the duration of a dot. The time between two letters is equal to three dots. The time between two words is equal to seven dots.

ALPHABET AND OTHER SIGNS

A	• —	J	• — — —	S	• • •		
B	— • • •	K	— • —	T	—		
C	— • — •	L	• — • •	U	• • —		
D	— • •	M	— —	V	• • • —		
E	•	N	— •	W	• — —		
F	• • — •	O	— — —	X	— • • —		
G	— — •	P	• — — •	Y	— • — —		
H	• • • •	Q	— — • —	Z	— — • •		
I	• •	R	• — •				

NUMERALS

1	• — — — —
2	• • — — —
3	• • • — —
4	• • • • —
5	• • • • •
6	— • • • •
7	— — • • •
8	— — — • •
9	— — — — •
0	— — — — —

PUNCTUATION AND OTHER SIGNS

Period • — • — • —
Question mark • • — — • •

Understand • — •
Error • • • • • • • •

Start — • —
End of message • — • — •

SOS • • • — — — • • •

1. Build a circuit that will allow you to send a Morse code message.

2. Write your name in Morse code.

   Send your name to your partner using your circuit.

3. Write a sentence in Morse code below and send it to your partner.

4. Decode your partner's message and write it in the space below.

Connecting Learning

1. How does your telegraph work?

2. How is the telegraph you built different from real telegraphs?

3. Why aren't telegraphs used widely today?

4. What devices have replaced the telegraph for communicating over long distances?

5. What are you wondering now?

The CLICK Heard Around the WORLD

Topic
Energy transformation

Key Question
What is the transfer of energy that we used to send messages?

Learning Goals
Students will:
- construct a simple electromagnet;
- use the electromagnet to make a model of a telegraph key;
- use the model to send the international distress signal, SOS, as a series of clicks; and
- trace the transformation of energy that occurs.

Guiding Documents
Project 2061 Benchmark
- *Energy appears in different forms. Heat energy is in the disorderly motion of molecules and in radiation; chemical energy is in the arrangement of atoms; mechanical energy is in moving bodies or in elasticity distorted shapes; and electrical energy is in the attraction or repulsion between charges.*

NRC Standard
- *Energy is a property of many substances and is associated with heat, light, electricity, mechanical motion, sound, nuclei, and the nature of a chemical. Energy is transferred in many ways.*

Science
Physical science
   electricity
      circuits
   energy transformations

Integrated Processes
Observing
Comparing and contrasting
Applying
Modeling

Materials
Nails, 3 inch (10 penny)
Insulated wire
Wire stripper
Metal washers, 3/8-inch diameter
Glue
Scissors
D cells
Battery holders

Masking tape
Pencils
Pattern pages (see *Management 5*)
Construction pages
Student pages

Background Information
One of the most important processes underlying the physical universe is the continual transformation of one form of energy to another form of energy. From photosynthesis, the transformation of light energy to the chemical energy contained in plants, to the burning of gasoline in our automobile engines that converts heat to the mechanical energy that moves our cars, everywhere one looks, nature transforms one form of energy to another form. This diagram shows the major forms of energy and illustrates the conversion paths between the various forms. In this activity, chemical energy is transformed to electrical energy which is transformed into sound energy (highlighted in this diagram).

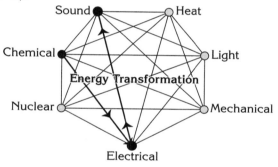

Students will build a simple model of a telegraph key. The model converts the chemical energy in a D-size battery to electrical energy to sound energy heard as an audible "click." The model uses an electromagnet. An electromagnet creates a magnetic field when electricity runs through it. As soon as the electricity stops, the magnetic field disappears. In an electromagnet, the magnetic field can be switched on and off.

Samuel Morse worked as an artist but upon overhearing a conversation about the newly discovered electromagnet, he realized that the electromagnet could be used to communicate over long distances. He was awarded a patent for the electric telegraph in 1854. With his telegraph, a key pressed in one location caused another key in a distant location to "click." Morse also invented a code that converts the letters of the alphabet, the 10 digits, and a few punctuation marks into dots and dashes or, as they are sometimes described, "dits" and "dahs." For example, the letter "A" is dot-dash and the number one is dot-dash-dash-dash-dash.

Key Vocabulary

Chemical energy: the energy stored in the chemicals of the battery (most alkaline batteries contain zinc and manganese oxide)

Electrical energy: the energy associated with electrical charge moving through a conductor like a wire

Electromagnet: the magnetic field created when electricity travels through a wire-wrapped metal rod

Energy transformation: the conversion of energy from one form to another

Morse code: the representation of letters of the alphabet and the digits zero through nine as "dots" and "dashes"

SOS: international distress signal (dot dot dot / dash dash dash / dot dot dot)

Sound energy: a form of energy that has to have a solid, liquid, or gas through which to travel

Telegraph: an electrical device that transmits coded messages along wires, over long distances

Management

1. Purchase a box of steel, three-inch nails (10-penny) and a package of metal washers, 3/8 inch in diameter, at your local home improvement store.
2. Insulated wire (item number 1968) is available from AIMS.
3. This activity was tested using both one- and two-meter lengths of wire. The longer wire length makes a slightly stronger electromagnet and is preferred, but, if the amount of wire is limited, one-meter lengths will work.
4. Use a wire stripper to remove at least one inch of insulation from each end of the wire. Wire strippers (item number 1970) are available from AIMS.
5. Copy the *Electromagnet Base Patterns* page, the *Sound Arm Patterns* page, and the *Telegraph Base Patterns* page on card stock. Each page contains more than one pattern. Use scissors to separate the patterns and organize them into three-pattern sets for easy distribution to students. Each group will need one set of the three patterns.
6. The electromagnet requires one D-size battery in a holder as a source of electrical energy. Battery holders can be ordered from AIMS (item number 1960). Attach an 8-centimeter length of wire (stripped at each end) to one side of the battery holder. Prepare one holder for each group.

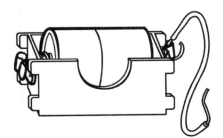

If you do not have battery holders, you can stretch a rubber band lengthwise around the battery and then secure the rubber band to the battery by wrapping masking tape around the battery. The rubber band will hold the stripped end of the wire in place.

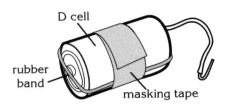

7. Before doing this activity with students, construct and test your own model telegraph. Doing so will make it easier for you to anticipate any problems your students might have and give you time to plan corrective actions.

Procedure

Constructing the Model Telegraph

1. Introduce or review the major forms of energy and energy transformations.
2. Introduce or review the techniques for working with card stock (see the *How to Cut, Score, and Glue Card Stock* page).
3. Organize the students into groups of at least two. Winding the electromagnet and other construction steps are easier to do if students assist each other.
4. Distribute the first page of construction instructions to each group along with the necessary materials.
5. Allow time for groups to follow the instructions and construct the electromagnet, the base, and the sound arm. Move among the groups providing assistance as necessary.
6. When groups are done, distribute the second page of construction instructions and the remaining materials.
7. Instruct students to complete their model telegraphs and test them.

Troubleshooting the Model Telegraph

1. Check the wire connections at the battery.
2. Check the connection at the electromagnet.
3. Check that the head of the nail and the washer are approximately one-sixteenth of an inch apart. If not, slide the electromagnet forward or backward to adjust the distance.
4. Touch the wires together again and check for an audible click.
5. If necessary, readjust the distance between the head of the nail and the metal washer. [Note: There should be enough "spring" in the sound arm so that it pulls away from the head of the nail when the electromagnet is not powered.]

Using the Model Telegraph

1. Distribute the first student page to each student.
2. Explain to the students that a *schematic* is a simplified drawing of a machine or electrical device that shows how the separate parts are connected. Tell the students to complete the schematic drawing of their model telegraphs and answer the remaining questions on the page.
3. Distribute the second student page. Explain how to use the *Morse Code Chart* to translate letters of the alphabet into dots and dashes, and do several examples together as a class.
4. When students understand how to use the chart, have them use it to code SOS, the international signal for distress, and then send the signal to others in the group using their model telegraphs.
5. Allow time for students to convert their names to Morse code and to practice sending messages on their model telegraphs.
6. Discuss what students learned and how this is an example of chemical energy being changed into electrical energy being changed into sound energy.

Connecting Learning

1. How does the electromagnet make your telegraph model work? [When the free ends of the wire are touched, electricity from the battery flows through the wire wrapped around the nail creating a magnetic field that attracts the metal washer. When the wires are separated, electricity no longer flows around the nail and the magnetic field disappears.]
2. What part of your model contains chemical energy? [the battery]
3. What kind of energy is produced by the transformation of the chemical energy? [electrical energy]
4. Where in your model is electrical energy converted to sound energy? [at the sound arm or metal washer]
5. What other examples can you think of where electrical energy is transformed to sound energy? [doorbell, phone ringing, radio, mp3 players, etc.]
6. What are you wondering now?

Extensions

1. Open a paper clip, bend it into an "L" shape, and tape it behind the washer side of the sound arm. Now, a "click" followed by a "clack" can be heard as the sound arm hits the paper clip when the switch to the electromagnet is opened.

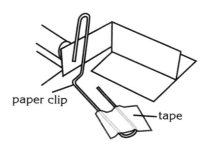

paper clip

tape

2. Improve on the design, durability, and operation of the simple model constructed in this activity. An Internet search will yield several wood and metal models from which to choose.
3. Construct two devices that can be placed at widely separated locations and used to transmit coded messages between the two locations.

The CLICK Heard Around the WORLD

Key Question

What is the transfer of energy that we used to send messages?

Learning Goals

Students will:

- construct a simple electromagnet;

- use the electromagnet to make a model of a telegraph key;

- use the model to send the international distress signal, SOS, as a series of clicks; and

- trace the transformation of energy that occurs.

The CLICK Heard Around the WORLD

How to Cut, Score, and Glue Card Stock

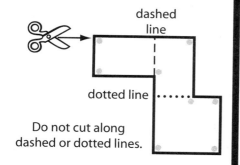

dashed line

dotted line

Do not cut along dashed or dotted lines.

Cutting to a Corner

Every piece of a card stock pattern will be outlined in solid black lines. The pattern may also contain dashed and/or dotted lines. Always cut along the solid black lines. Never cut along dashed or dotted lines. Whenever possible, cut to a corner. This prevents you from accidentally creasing or folding the piece and makes for easier cutting.

Scoring

It is easy to neatly fold card stock if the line along which you wish to fold is first traced over with a ballpoint pen or pencil. This is called scoring. (Ballpoint pens that are out of ink are ideal for this purpose.) Use a ruler to score along dashed and dotted lines.

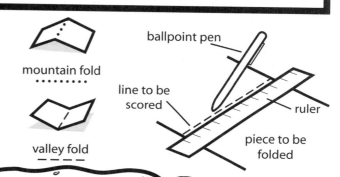

mountain fold

valley fold

ballpoint pen

line to be scored

ruler

piece to be folded

Gluing

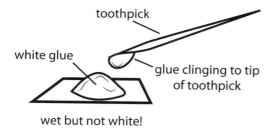

toothpick

white glue

glue clinging to tip of toothpick

wet but not white!

For large areas, using a glue stick is the fastest and easiest way to glue card stock. Be sure to press hard on the glued sections. If possible, use a paper clip to clamp the pieces together. For small areas or where maximum strength is needed, use white glue. Nothing will ruin a project faster than the application of too much white glue. Put a bean-sized drop of glue on a piece of card stock left over from cutting out the pattern. Dip the end of a round toothpick in the glue, and apply only the glue clinging to the end of the toothpick to the piece to be glued. Use the end of the toothpick to spread the glue evenly over the surface of the piece.

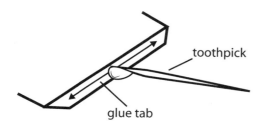

toothpick

glue tab

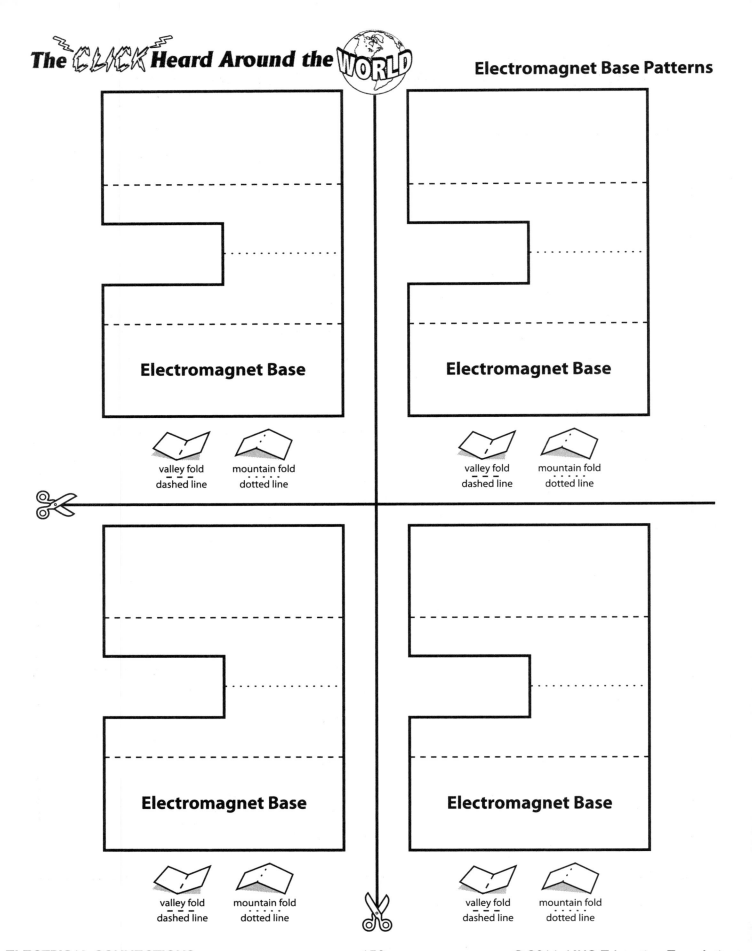

Electromagnet Base

valley fold
dashed line

mountain fold
dotted line

Electromagnet Base

valley fold
dashed line

mountain fold
dotted line

Electromagnet Base

valley fold
dashed line

mountain fold
dotted line

Electromagnet Base

valley fold
dashed line

mountain fold
dotted line

The CLICK Heard Around the WORLD

Sound Arm Patterns

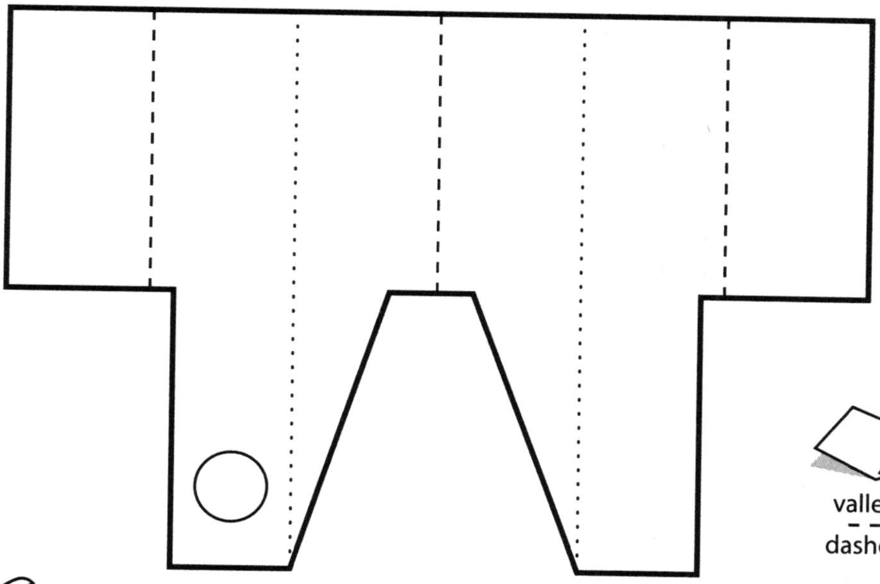

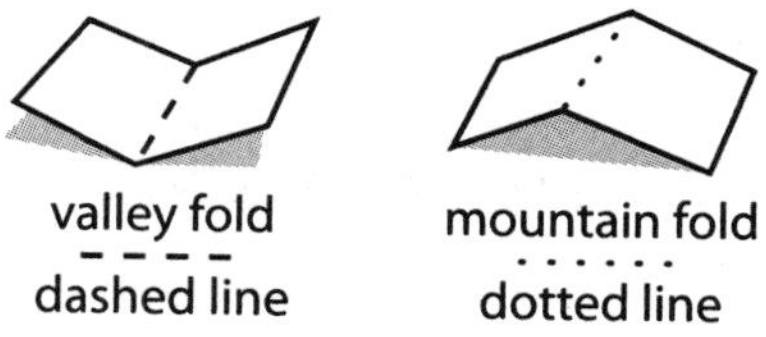

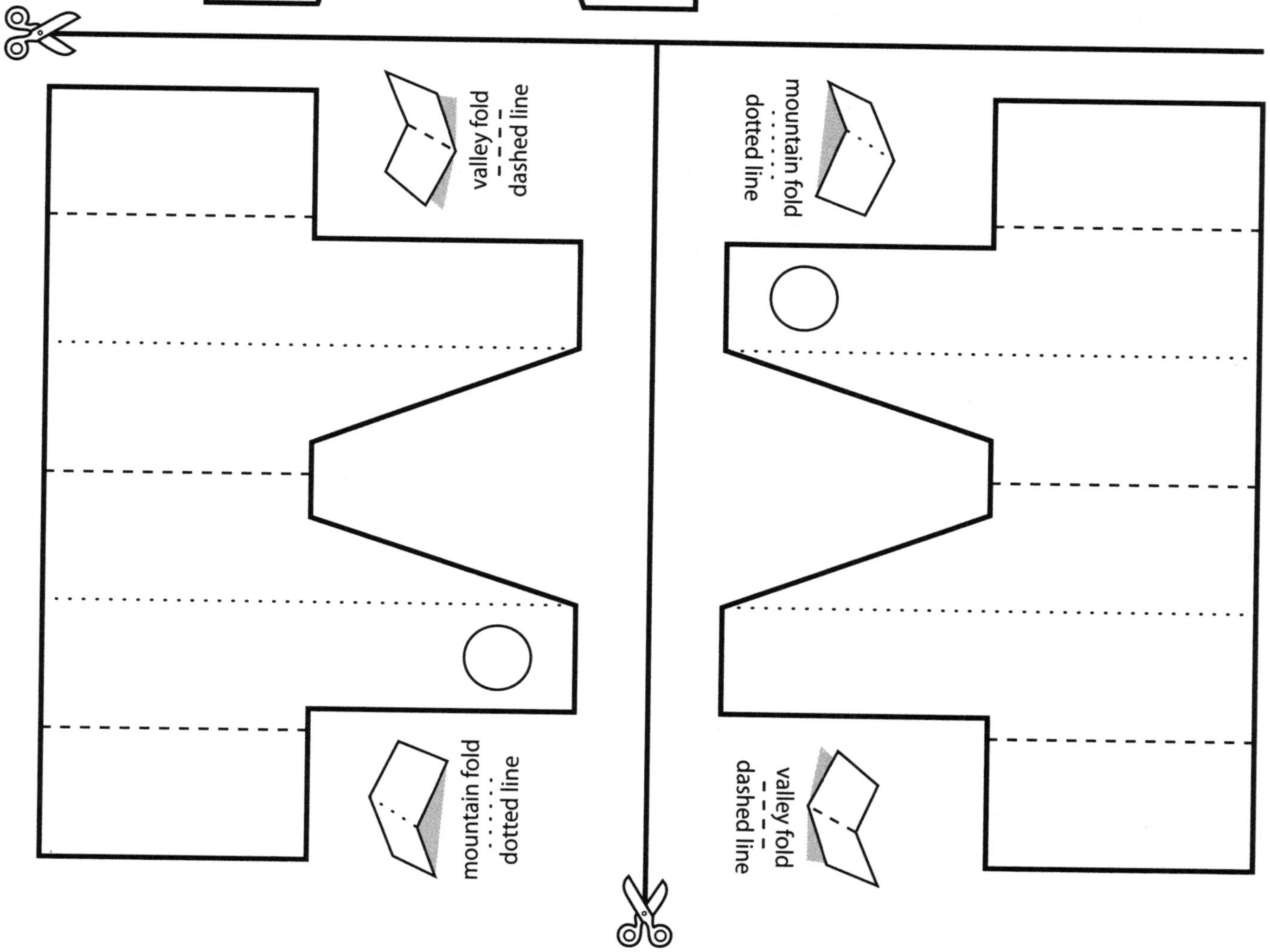

valley fold
- - - - -
dashed line

mountain fold
· · · · ·
dotted line

valley fold
- - - - -
dashed line

mountain fold
· · · · ·
dotted line

mountain fold
· · · · ·
dotted line

valley fold
- - - - -
dashed line

© 2011 AIMS Education Foundation

The CLICK Heard Around the WORLD

Telegraph Base Patterns

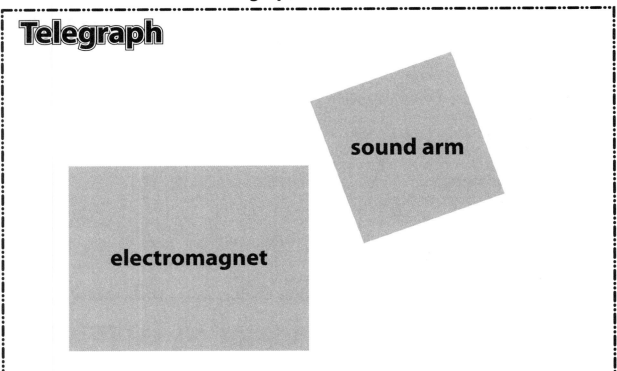

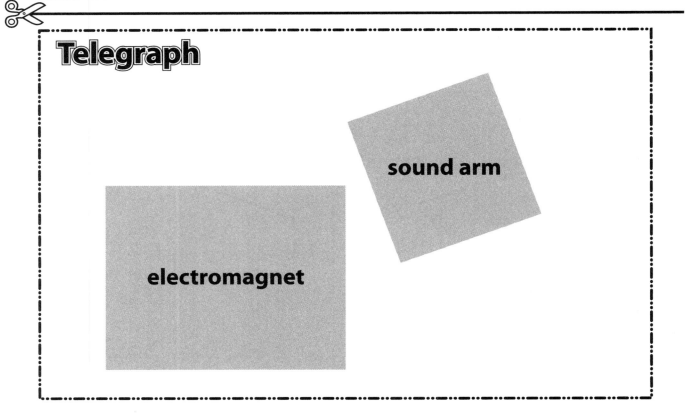

The CLICK Heard Around the WORLD

Materials
One nail
Wire, 2 meters
Masking tape

Electromagnet Base pattern
Scissors
Sound Arm pattern

Pencil
Glue

Winding the Electromagnet

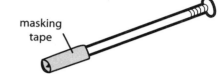

masking tape

1. Wrap the masking tape around the sharp end of the nail.

2. Work with a partner to wrap the wire around the nail. One person holds the nail and the other wraps the wire.

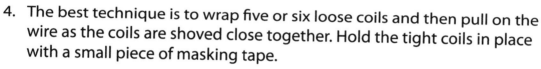

4 cm   loose coils   tight coils

3. Leave about 4 centimeters free at one end of the wire. Start wrapping at the edge of the masking tape.

4. The best technique is to wrap five or six loose coils and then pull on the wire as the coils are shoved close together. Hold the tight coils in place with a small piece of masking tape.

   Keep wrapping until two layers have been wrapped around the nail leaving 4 cm free at the remaining end of the wire.

Making the Electromagnet Base and Sound Arm

1. Cut out the *Electromagnetic Base* along the solid line. Score along the dashed and dotted lines. Mountain fold and valley fold the pattern and then set it aside.

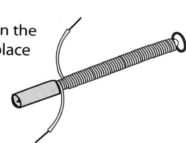

mountain fold
valley fold

2. Cut out the *Sound Arm* pattern. Score along the dashed and dotted lines. Mountain and valley fold the figure.

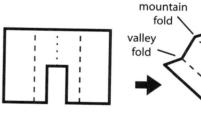

3. Apply glue to the inside of the first long arm and press flat. Apply glue to the inside of the second long arm and press flat.

4. Apply glue to one of the valley sections between the two long arms, and press the whole figure flat.

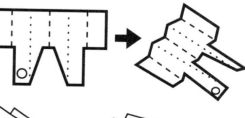

apply glue

long arm

sound arm piece

The CLICK Heard Around the WORLD

Materials
Electromagnet Base piece
Pencil

Glue
Metal washer

Telegraph Base piece
D cell (battery) in holder

Assembling the Telegraph

1. Take the *Electromagnet Base* piece and place a pencil inside the piece along the length of the dotted line at the top of the piece. Shape the card stock around the pencil. Open the piece and apply glue to the shaded area.

2. Insert the electromagnet in the rounded top of the piece. Press the sides together so that the sides of the piece just below the electromagnet are glued together.

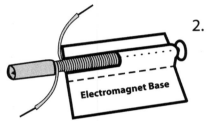

3. Glue the washer over the circle on the *Sound Arm* piece. Bend the arm with the washer so that it forms an "L" shape with the base of the piece.

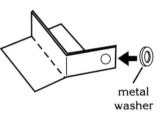

4. Glue the *Electromagnet Base* piece on the shaded area of the *Telegraph Base* labeled *electromagnet*. Be sure the head of the nail faces the right edge of the base.

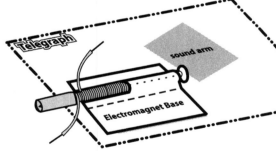

5. Glue the *Sound Arm* piece to the shaded area labeled *sound arm*. Check that the metal washer is almost, but not quite, touching the head of the nail.

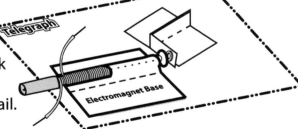

6. Connect one side of the battery holder to one of the wires on the electromagnet.

7. Touch the ends of the remaining wires together and observe whether or not the electromagnet attracts the metal washer with an audible "click."

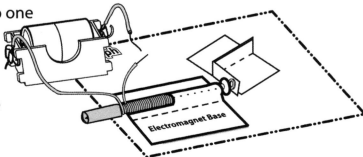

 © 2011 AIMS Education Foundation

The CLICK Heard Around the WORLD

1. Complete the schematic drawing of your telegraph model by labeling the different parts and then drawing in the lines (wires) that show how the parts of the model are connected.

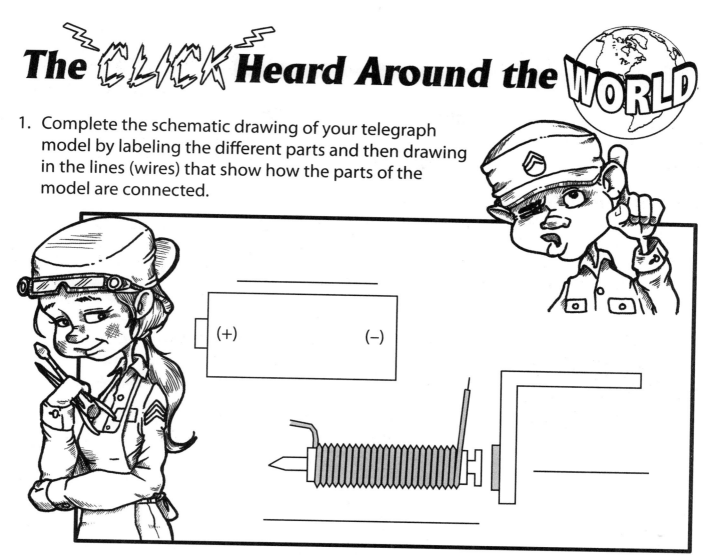

(+)   (−)

2. What part of your model provides electrical energy?

3. Describe how an electromagnet works.

4. Where in your model is electrical energy transformed to sound energy?

The *CLICK* Heard Around the WORLD

The letters of the alphabet and the 10 digits can be translated into dots and dashes by using the following chart. Start at the top and move down and to the left or right until you reach the desired letter. Each move left is coded as a dash. Each move to the right is a dot.

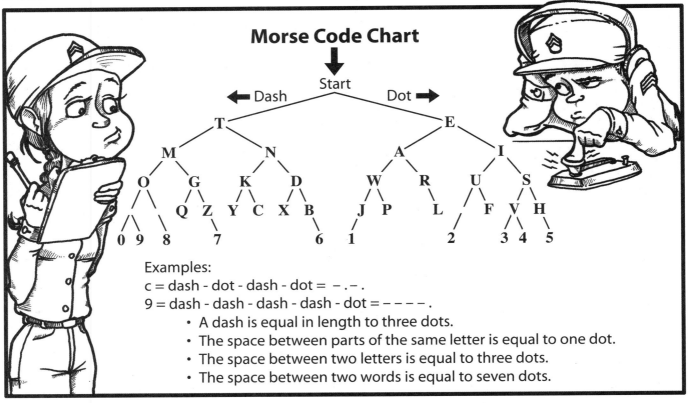

Morse Code Chart

Examples:
c = dash - dot - dash - dot = − . − .
9 = dash - dash - dash - dash - dot = − − − − .
  • A dash is equal in length to three dots.
  • The space between parts of the same letter is equal to one dot.
  • The space between two letters is equal to three dots.
  • The space between two words is equal to seven dots.

1. The international distress signal is SOS. Use the Morse code chart to translate SOS into the dots and dashes.

    SOS = _____

2. Send an SOS signal on your model telegraph.

3. Convert your first and last name to Morse code.

    First Name = _____

    Last Name = _____

The CLICK Heard Around the WORLD

Connecting Learning

1. How does the electromagnet make your telegraph model work?

2. What part of your model contains chemical energy?

3. What kind of energy is produced by the transformation of the chemical energy?

4. Where in your model is electrical energy converted to sound energy?

5. What other examples can you think of where electrical energy is transformed to sound energy?

6. What are you wondering now?

 © 2011 AIMS Education Foundation

We use electromagnets every day. They are a part of all of these common devices:

- Loudspeakers
- Electric motors
- Generators
- Doorbells
- Computer hard drives

There's an electromagnet in my hard drive... really?!

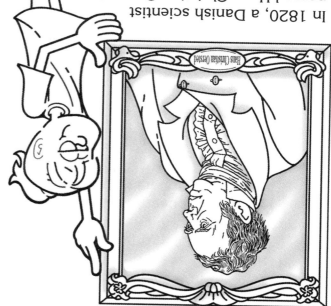

In 1820, a Danish scientist named Hans Christian Oersted made an important discovery. He noticed that an electric current in a wire deflected the magnetic needle of a nearby compass.

Our lives would be very different today if electromagnets had never been invented.

ELECTROMAGNETISM

His discovery led to the invention of the electromagnet. An electromagnet is a magnet that is created by electric current. A wire connected to a battery makes a simple electromagnet. When the current is on, there is a magnetic field. When the current is off, there is no magnetic field.

Think of a giant crane in a junkyard. It has an electromagnet at the end. When electric current is on, the crane can pick up cars and other things containing iron. It moves them to a new location. Then, the current is turned off, and the cars drop to the ground.

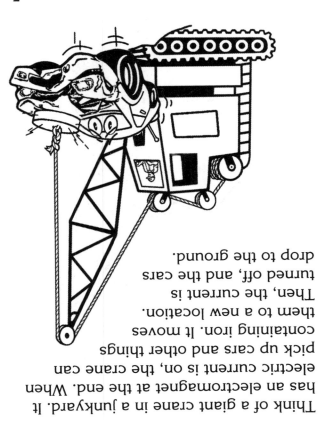

This made him realize that electricity and magnetism are related. An electric current produces a magnetic field. A change in a magnetic field can also produce an electric current.

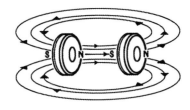

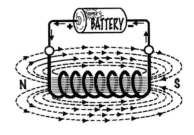

The strength of an electromagnet can be increased in several ways.

- The wire can be wound into a coil. The more coils, the stronger the electromagnet. (Each coil acts like a separate magnet.)
- The voltage of the current going through the wire can be increased.
- A metal core, such as a nail or a bolt, can be used. (The magnetic field produced by the current in the coils induces a magnetic field in the iron core.)

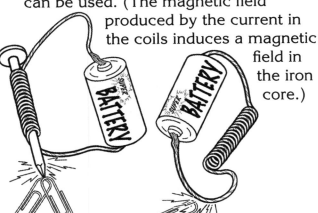

© 2011 AIMS Education Foundation

The Electromagnetic Connection

Topic
Electromagnetism

Key Question
What is the relationship between electricity and magnetism?

Learning Goal
Students will discover the relationship between electricity and magnetism.

Guiding Documents
Project 2061 Benchmarks
- *Without touching them, material that has been electrically charged pulls on all other materials and may either push or pull on other charged materials.*
- *Electric currents and magnets can exert a force on each other.*

NRC Standards
- *Ask a question about objects and events in the environment.*
- *Employ simple equipment and tools to gather data and extend the senses.*
- *Electricity in circuits can produce light, heat, sound, and magnetic effects. Electrical circuits require a complete loop through which an electrical current can pass.*

Science
Physical science
   electromagnetism

Integrated Processes
Observing
Comparing and contrasting
Drawing conclusions

Materials
For each group:
   20-cm wire with ends stripped
   D cell
   directional compass
   magnet

For each student:
   student page

Background Information
One of the key discoveries in the history of science was made in 1820 when the Danish physicist Hans Christian Oersted accidentally discovered that an electric current in a wire deflected the magnetic needle of a nearby compass. This discovery led to the realization that electricity and magnetism are related. Scientists later discovered that electricity and magnetism are simply two aspects of the same fundamental electromagnetic force.

Oersted's discovery paved the way for the invention of electromagnets, electric motors, electric generators, and other devices that have radically changed the world in which we live. These devices are based on two fundamental principles:
1. moving electric charges create a magnetic field, and
2. moving magnetic fields create electric fields.

Management
1. Students should work in groups of three or four.
2. Wire (item number 1968), directional compasses (item number 1990), and magnets (item number 1971) are available from AIMS.

Procedure
1. Discuss the *Key Question:* "What is the relationship between electricity and magnetism?"
2. Distribute a compass to each group and the student page to each student.
3. Have students place the compass on a flat surface and rotate its base. The needle will continue to point in the same direction because it is affected by the Earth's magnetic field. Discuss this and have students write their explanations in the space provided.
4. Distribute a magnet to each group and have students bring it near the compass. The magnet will deflect the needle. Have students write their observations in the space provided.
5. Distribute a D cell and wire to each group. Have them connect the wire to the terminals of the cell and bring the wire near the compass needle. It will be deflected, proving that an electric current creates a magnetic field. Have students write their observations in the space provided. It is important to note that a current is present in the wire when the wire is connected to the terminals of the cell, even though it is not directly observable without seeing its effects on a compass.

                    © 2011 AIMS Education Foundation

6. Have students disconnect the wire and hold it next to the compass. The needle will not be deflected. Invite students to write their observations in the space provided.
7. Discuss the results of this activity and have students write their conclusions at the bottom of the sheet.

Connecting Learning
1. What happens when the compass is placed on a flat surface and its base rotated? [The needle continues to point in the same direction.]
2. Why does this happen? [The needle is aligning itself with the Earth's magnetic field.]
3. What happens when a magnet is brought near the compass? [The needle is deflected.]
4. Why does this happen? [When the magnet is near the compass, its magnetic field is stronger than the Earth's magnetic field and it deflects the needle.]
5. What happens when the wire connected to the D cell is brought near the compass? [The needle is deflected.]
6. What does this prove? [An electric current produces a magnetic field.]
7. What are you wondering now?

Extensions
1. Try different lengths of wire and see if there is a difference.
2. Reverse the cell and note the difference.

Curriculum Correlation
Social Studies
Have students research the role Oersted's discovery played in the history of electricity.

Science
Have students study how electric generators and electric motors work and relate this knowledge to Oersted's discovery.

 © 2011 AIMS Education Foundation

The Electromagnetic Connection

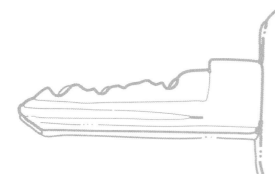

Key Question

What is the relationship between electricity and magnetism?

Learning Goal

Students will:

discover the relationship between electricity and magnetism.

© 2011 AIMS Education Foundation

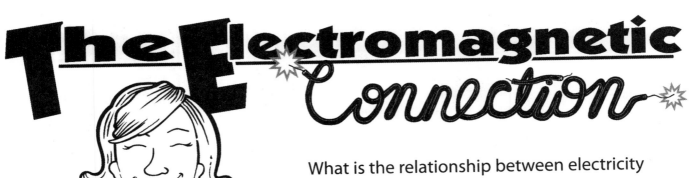

The Electromagnetic Connection

What is the relationship between electricity and magnetism?
Find out!

You will need:

- a magnetic compass
- a magnet
- a D cell
- a 20-cm wire with the ends stripped

1. Place the compass flat on your desk and rotate its base. What do you notice? Why does the compass needle always point in the same direction?

2. Bring a magnet close to the compass. What happens?

3. Connect the wire to the terminals of the D cell. Now bring the wire close to the compass. What happens?

4. Disconnect the wire from the D cell. Bring the wire close to the compass again. What happens now?

5. What would this lead you to conclude?

The Electromagnetic Connection

Connecting Learning

1. What happens when the compass is placed on a flat surface and its base rotated?

2. Why does this happen?

3. What happens when a magnet is brought near the compass?

4. Why does this happen?

5. What happens when the wire connected to the D cell is brought near the compass?

6. What does this prove?

7. What are you wondering now?

 © 2011 AIMS Education Foundation

Make a Galvanometer!

Topic
Galvanometers

Key Question
What is a galvanometer?

Learning Goals
Students will:
- construct a galvanometer, and
- observe the movement of the galvanometer's needle as it detects small amounts of electric current.

Guiding Documents
Project 2061 Benchmarks
- *Without touching them, material that has been electrically charged pulls on all other materials and may either push or pull on other charged materials.*
- *Electric currents and magnets can exert a force on each other.*

NRC Standards
- *Ask a question about objects and events in the environment.*
- *Employ simple equipment and tools to gather data and extend the senses.*
- *Electricity in circuits can produce light, heat, sound, and magnetic effects. Electrical circuits require a complete loop through which an electrical current can pass.*

Science
Physical science
  magnetism
  electricity
    electric current

Integrated Processes
Observing
Comparing and contrasting
Drawing conclusions

Materials
For each group:
  50 cm of insulated wire with ends stripped
  D cell
  directional compass

For each student:
  student page

Background Information
When a current flows through a wire, it creates a magnetic field that surrounds the wire. The polarity of this magnetic field depends on the direction of the current in the wire. The strength of the magnetic field depends on the amount of current flowing through the wire. For any set amount of current, the magnetic field around a wire can be strengthened by coiling the wire. The more coils a wire has, the stronger the magnetic field produced by a given current.

Johann Schweigger, a German physicist, built the first galvanometer shortly after Oersted's discovery of the connection between electricity and magnetism. A galvanometer is a device that detects and measures small electric currents. Schweigger's galvanometer consisted of a magnetized needle surrounded by a coil of wire. When an electric current was present in the coil, it created a magnetic field that deflected the needle. When the current to the coil was reversed, the needle was deflected in the opposite direction. Modern galvanometers are similar to the galvanometer built by Schweigger and the one made in this lesson.

Management
1. Students should be in groups of three or four.
2. This activity can be done on the same day as *The Electromagnetic Connection.*
3. Insulated wire (item number 1968), wire strippers (item number 1970), and directional compasses (item number 1990) are available from AIMS.

Procedure
1. Discuss the *Key Question:* "What is a galvanometer?"
2. Distribute materials to each group.
3. Have students build a galvanometer following the instructions on the activity sheet.
4. Direct them to connect the D cell to the galvanometer and observe what happens. Have students record their observations.
5. Now direct them to reverse the D cell and connect it to the galvanometer once more. Have them observe what happens and record observations.
6. Discuss the results and ask students to write conclusions at the bottom of the activity sheet.

Connecting Learning

1. What happens when the D cell is attached to the galvanometer? [The compass needle is deflected.]
2. Why does this happen? [The current in the coil of wire creates a magnetic field that interacts with the magnetic field of the compass.]
3. What happens when the D cell is reversed? [The needle is deflected in the opposite direction.]
4. What does this prove? [The direction of the current determines the polarity of the magnetic field.]
5. What are you wondering now?

Extensions

1. Use different gauges or lengths of wire for the galvanometer.
2. Try more than one cell (or older cells) and note the difference.

MAKE a Galvanometer!

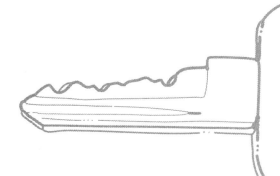

Key Question

What is a galvanometer?

Learning Goals

Students will:

- construct a galvanometer, and

- observe the movement of the galvanometer's needle as it detects small amounts of electric current.

MAKE a Galvanometer!

What is a galvanometer?

It is an instrument that detects the presence of small amounts of electric current.

To build your own galvanometer, you will need:
- 50 cm insulated wire with ends stripped
- a directional compass
- a D cell

1. Rotate the bezel so the needle points at the "N" on the compass.

2. Wrap the wire around the compass in an east-west orientation, leaving about 10 cm free at each end.

3. Attach the ends of the wire to the terminals of the D cell.

What happens?

Reverse the D cell and attach the ends of the wires again.

What happens?

Conclusions:

Connecting Learning

1. What happens when the D cell is attached to the galvanometer?

2. Why does this happen?

3. What happens when the D cell is reversed?

4. What does this prove?

5. What are you wondering now?

Electromagnetic Explorations

Topic
Electromagnets

Key Question
What happens to the poles of an electromagnet when you reverse the direction of the current flowing through it?

Learning Goals
Students will:
- build a simple electromagnet and test its properties,
- use a directional compass to determine orientation of the electromagnet's poles, and
- observe the effect the direction of current flow through the electromagnet has on this orientation.

Guiding Documents
Project 2061 Benchmarks
- *Without touching them, a magnet pulls on all things made of iron and either pushes or pulls on other magnets.*
- *Without touching them, material that has been electrically charged pulls on all other materials and may either push or pull other charged materials.*
- *Electric currents and magnets can exert a force on each other.*

NRC Standard
- *Electricity in circuits can produce light, heat, sound, and magnetic effects. Electrical circuits require a complete loop through which an electrical current can pass.*

Science
Physical science
  magnetism
  electromagnets

Integrated Processes
Observing
Predicting
Collecting and recording data
Comparing and contrasting
Interpreting data
Reporting and communicating data

Materials
For each group:
  directional compass
  large nail (8 d or 10 d)
  50 cm of insulated copper wire with the ends stripped
  D cell
  paper clips

Background Information
One of the key discoveries of all time was that electricity and magnetism are closely connected. Moving electric charges (an electric current) create a magnetic field. Conversely, a moving magnetic field creates an electric current (in conducting materials). The discovery of this electromagnetic connection in the 19th century led to the invention of the electromagnet, the electric motor, and the electric generator. While the electric generator is arguably the most important of these inventions in terms of its impact on technology, this activity will explore the much simpler electromagnet.

Iron and other magnetic materials contain *magnetic domains*, which are microscopic clusters of billions of atoms that are aligned magnetically making each domain a miniature magnet. In most magnetic materials, these domains point in random directions and cancel each other's magnetic fields. In permanent magnets, however, many of these domains are aligned magnetically and produce a net magnetic field.

Magnetic materials like iron that are not permanent magnets become temporary magnets in the presence of a magnetic field. This field causes the magnetic domains to temporarily align with each other. As long as the magnetic field is present, the material acts like a magnet. When the magnetic field is removed, the domains go back to their random arrangement and the material no longer acts like a magnet.

Since an electric current produces a magnetic field, an electromagnet can be made by coiling wire around a piece of iron. When current flows through this coil, it produces a magnetic field that causes the magnetic domains in the iron core to temporarily align, turning it into a magnet. (Scientists say that the magnetic field produced by the current *induces* a magnetic field in the iron.) As soon as the current stops, the magnetic field is no longer present, the magnetic domains in the core go back to their original alignments, and the iron no longer acts like a magnet.

Electromagnets play an important role in technology. Large, powerful electromagnets attached to cranes are used in factories and junkyards to lift and move heavy pieces of steel or iron. Smaller electromagnets are utilized in the electromagnetic switches called solenoids. These switches are used in cars, doorbells, and many other mechanical devices.

Just like permanent magnets, electromagnets have north and south magnetic poles. The direction of current flow through an electromagnet determines which pole is north and which is south. Reversing the flow of electricity reverses the orientation of the poles.

To determine which pole is which in this activity, a directional (magnetic) compass is used. The magnetized needle of the compass normally aligns itself with the Earth's magnetic field. The end that points north is the "north-seeking" pole, or north pole, for short. The other end is the "south-seeking" or south pole. Since opposite magnetic poles attract and like poles repel, when a magnet's north pole is brought near a compass, the south pole of the compass is attracted while the north pole is simultaneously repelled. Bringing the south pole of a magnet near the compass has the opposite effect, attracting the north pole of the compass and repelling the south. In this manner, the poles of any unmarked magnet, like the electromagnets students construct in this activity, can be determined.

Management

1. *Caution*: In this activity students build a simple electromagnet. While they cannot be shocked by holding the wires from the electromagnet on the terminals of the D cell, they may be startled by the heat produced if they hold the wires on too long (more than 10-15 seconds at a time). Be sure to emphasize that if students feel the wire getting hot, they need to let it go and break the circuit.

2. Optional: Wide rubber bands can be used to hold the wires to the D cells. If you choose to do this, caution students not to leave the D cells connected to the electromagnets for more than 15-20 seconds at a time since the energy in the D cells will drain very quickly.

3. This activity has two parts that are intended to be done sequentially. In the first part, students construct an electromagnet and explore its properties. In the second part, students use a magnetic compass to determine how the poles of the electromagnet are affected by the direction of current flow.

4. If you don't have enough compasses, you can do *Part One* as a whole class activity and then let students do *Part Two* as a center.

5. Directional compasses (item number 1990) insulated wire (item number 1968), and wire strippers (item number 1970) are available from AIMS.

Procedure

Part One

1. Divide students into small groups. Hand out the first student page and the materials for making the electromagnets.

2. Demonstrate how to coil the wire around the nail and then have students do the same. (See the student page for *Part One* for an illustration.)

3. Direct students to try the first task listed—attempting to pick up paper clips with the nail and coiled wire they have just made. Have students record their observations. (They will be unable to pick up any paper clips because this apparatus is not a magnet.)

4. Demonstrate how to connect the ends of the wires to the terminals of a D cell by holding them in place with a thumb and finger. Reassure students that doing this will not shock them, but explain that the wire *might* get hot if it is held on the D cell too long. Tell them that if this happens, all they have to do is to remove the wire from the battery terminals and it will quickly cool.

5. Have students connect their electromagnets to the D cells and try to pick up the paper clips. They will discover that as long as current is flowing through the coil, the electromagnet can pick up and hold several paper clips (with both ends of the nail). When students stop the flow of electricity, the paper clips will probably drop off since the electromagnet is no longer working. (In some rare cases however, the nail may have become magnetized enough in the process to continue to hold on to one or two paper clips.)

6. Encourage students to see what other things their electromagnets can pick up. Have them record their findings.

7. The last task in this part asks students to try and pick up paper clips once more with the nail and coil. They will probably not be able to do this since the electromagnet only works when a current is flowing through the coil. However, as mentioned above, in some cases the nail may have become magnetized enough that it will pick up a paper clip or two.

8. Have students share their results before going on to the next part.

Part Two

1. Hand out the second student page and a directional compass to each group.

2. Explain how a directional compass can be used to determine the poles of any unmarked magnet. (See *Background Information*.)

3. Have students follow the steps listed on the page to determine the poles of their electromagnet. They will record this data by sketching their magnet and labeling its poles.

4. Ask students to predict what might happen to the poles of the electromagnet if the direction of the current is reversed and then record these predictions on the page.
5. Have students reverse the D cell so that the wire that was attached to the positive terminal is now connected to the negative terminal and vice versa. Doing this makes the current flow in the opposite direction. Tell them to repeat these steps to see what happens to the poles of the electromagnet when the current is flowing in the opposite direction.
6. Tell students to record their findings and then close with a class discussion.

Connecting Learning
Part One
1. What happened when you tried to pick up the paper clips with the nail and coiled wire before it was attached to the D cell? [The nail and coil are not magnets so they can't pick up any paper clips.]
2. What happened when you tried to pick up the paper clips when the nail and coiled wire were attached to the D cell? [The nail and coil apparatus became an electromagnet when current was flowing through the wire. The electromagnet was able to pick up the paper clips.]
3. What happened when the wire connected to the D cell was let go? [The paper clips dropped off since the electromagnet must have a current flowing through it in order to operate.]
4. With the D cell disconnected, were you able to pick up any paper clips? [No. Since there is no current, the nail and coil are no longer magnetic. Optional answer: Yes. In some rare cases the nail becomes magnetized enough while the current is flowing through the coil that it becomes a permanent magnet.]
5. What other things were you able to pick up with your electromagnet? [Any small magnetic objects (usually made of steel or iron) can be picked up by the electromagnet.]

Part Two
1. Why does the needle of a directional compass point north and south? [The needle is a freely swinging magnet that aligns with the Earth's magnetic field.]
2. What do you know about the poles of magnets? [Opposite magnetic poles attract each other while like poles repel.]
3. How can you use a directional compass to determine the poles of your electromagnet? [The north pole of the electromagnet will attract the south-pointing end of the compass needle, while the south pole of the electromagnet will attract the north-pointing end of the needle.]

4. What happens to the flow of current through the electromagnet if you switch the wire on the positive terminal of the D cell to the negative terminal and vice versa? [The current will flow in the opposite direction.]
5. What effect does the reversed current have on the poles of the electromagnet? [When the current going through the electromagnet is reversed, the magnetic poles switch. The north pole becomes the south pole and vice versa.]
6. What are you wondering now?

Extensions
1. Remove the nail from the coil and test to see if it has become slightly magnetized. To do this, bring it near the compass and observe the results. [Most nails will have become weak magnets, complete with north and south poles. While the magnetic field of a nail magnet is not likely strong enough to lift paper clips, it is strong enough to deflect a compass needle. Try to think of a way to reverse the poles on this nail.]
2. Magnetize paper clips by stroking them with a powerful permanent magnet. Use the compass to determine the poles of the paper clips.

© 2011 AIMS Education Foundation

Electromagnetic Explorations

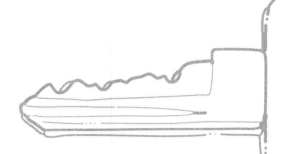

Key Question

What happens to the poles of an electromagnet when you reverse the direction of the current flowing through it?

Learning Goals

Students will:

- build a simple electromagnet and test its properties,

- use a directional compass to determine orientation of the electromagnet's poles, and

- observe the effect the direction of current flow through the electromagnet has on this orientation.

Electromagnetic Explorations

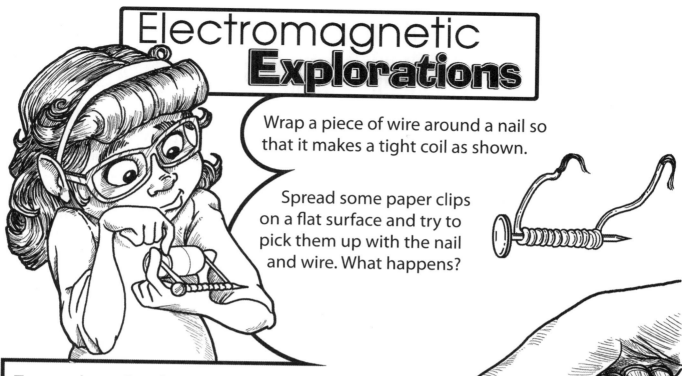

Wrap a piece of wire around a nail so that it makes a tight coil as shown.

Spread some paper clips on a flat surface and try to pick them up with the nail and wire. What happens?

To turn the nail and coil into an electromagnet, an electric current must flow through the coil. To do this, connect one end of the wire to the positive (+) terminal of the D cell, and the other end to the negative (-) terminal and hold these ends in place with your thumb and finger. This will not shock you, but the wire may get hot if you keep it connected too long. (If it does get too hot, just let go of the wire and it will cool down quickly.)

Try to pick up the paper clips with your electromagnet. What happens? Can you pick up paper clips with both ends of the nail? What other things can your electromagnet pick up?

Disconnect the D cell and try to pick up some paper clips once more. What do you notice? Why do you think this happens?

© 2011 AIMS Education Foundation

Electromagnetic Explorations

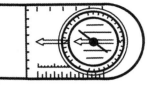

Your electromagnet acts like a permanent magnet when an electric current is flowing through it. Permanent magnets have a north and south pole that are often marked N and S. If the poles of a magnet are unmarked, a magnetic compass can be used to determine which pole is north and which one is south.

With the D cell connected, bring the pointed end of the nail in your electromagnet near the compass needle. What happens?

Next, bring the head of the nail near the compass needle. What happens this time?

From these results you can determine which end of the electromagnet is the north pole and which end is the south pole. Remember, opposite poles attract and like poles repel. Draw your electromagnet below and label the poles.

What do you think will happen if you reverse the D cell so that the current flows the opposite way through your electromagnet?

Repeat the experiment above with the opposite terminals of the D cell connected to the two wire ends of the electromagnet. What do you notice this time?

What conclusions can you draw from this experiment? (Write your conclusions on the back of this paper.)

 © 2011 AIMS Education Foundation

Electromagnetic Explorations

Connecting Learning

Part One

1. What happened when you tried to pick up the paper clips with the nail and coiled wire before it was attached to the D cell?

2. What happened when you tried to pick up the paper clips when the nail and coiled wire were attached to the D cell?

3. What happened when the wire connected to the D cell was let go?

4. What other things were you able to pick up with your electromagnet?

© 2011 AIMS Education Foundation

Electromagnetic Explorations

Connecting Learning

Part Two

1. Why does the needle of a directional compass point north and south?

2. What do you know about the poles of magnets?

3. How can you use a directional compass to determine the poles of your electromagnet?

4. What happens to the flow of current through the electromagnet if you switch the wire on the positive terminal of the D cell to the negative terminal and vice versa?

5. What effect does the reversed current have on the poles of the electromagnet?

6. What are you wondering now?

How to Make an ELECTRIC MOTOR

Topic
Electric motors

Key Question
How can we build an electric motor?

Learning Goal
Students will build a simple electric motor.

Guiding Documents
Project 2061 Benchmarks
- *Without touching them, a magnet pulls on all things made of iron and either pushes or pulls on other magnets.*
- *Without touching them, material that has been electrically charged pulls on all other materials and may either push or pull on other charged materials.*
- *Electric currents and magnets can exert a force on each other.*

NRC Standards
- *Design and conduct a scientific investigation.*
- *Employ simple equipment and tools to gather data and extend the senses.*
- *Electricity in circuits can produce light, heat, sound, and magnetic effects. Electrical circuits require a complete loop through which an electrical current can pass.*
- *Magnets attract and repel each other and certain kinds of other materials.*

Math
Measurement

Science
Physical science
 electricity
 magnetism
 motors

Integrated Processes
Observing
Controlling variables
Generalizing and applying

Materials
For each group:
 two D cells
 two jumbo (five cm long) metal paper clips
 modeling clay
 three ring magnets
 two 20-30 cm wires with ends stripped
 55 cm piece of 18-22 gauge magnet wire (copper wire coated with enamel)
 masking tape
 ruler
 scissors
 student pages

Background Information
An electric motor is a machine that changes electrical energy into mechanical energy. Electric motors are based on three principles: electric currents produce magnetic fields; the direction of the current determines the polarity of the magnetic field produced; and like magnetic poles repel while unlike poles attract.

A simple, direct-current electric motor consists of a coil of wire connected to a freely rotating shaft. The coil becomes an electromagnet when current goes through the wire. This coil and shaft assembly, called the *armature,* is positioned between two stationary permanent magnets with the north pole of one magnet and the south pole of the other magnet facing the armature. As current passes through the armature, it creates a magnetic field. When the armature's north pole is near the north pole of the stationary magnet, the armature is repelled and makes a half turn, approaching the south pole of the other permanent magnet to which it is attracted. Just as the armature reaches the south pole, the current to the armature is reversed (by a part called the *commutator).* This reversal of current causes the armature's north pole to become a south pole. Once again, two like poles are next to each other and the armature is repelled, making another half rotation. This process continues as long as current is present in the armature.

The motor built in this activity is not as complex as the one described above. It has no commutator to reverse the direction of the current and will not usually start unless its armature (coil) is given a spin. The coil only has current going through it half the time.

Here is how this motor works. As mentioned, the coil is given a spin. As the bottom half of the coil approaches the permanent magnet, the uninsulated part of its arms make electrical contact with the paper clips. This allows a current to flow through the coil making it an electromagnet. At this time the two magnets (electromagnet and permanent) will have the same or opposite polarity. If they have opposite polarity, they will be attracted to one another and the coil will move down toward the magnet with increased speed. If they have the same polarity, the coil and magnet will repel one another. If the coil is moving slowly, it may reverse its course, but if it has enough momentum to reach the magnet, the repulsion will push it upward (in the same direction) to start its next cycle. When the coil swings around, the current is interrupted, stopping the magnetic field for half a turn. When the current flows through the coil again, the two magnetic poles either repel or attract each other once more. After the coil starts spinning, momentum carries it through the part of its cycle when there is no current.

Management

1. Building an electric motor that works can be a frustrating experience. It may take much patience and repeated tinkering. It is highly advisable that the teacher build a working motor before doing this activity with students. This will provide an appreciation for the task and a working model for students to examine.
2. Students should work in groups of two to four.
3. This is an open-ended activity that allows many opportunities for discovery.
4. Be sure to use the type of wire specified in the materials list. Enameled wire is commonly called magnet wire; it is available from electronics stores and shops that repair electric motors.

Procedure

1. Discuss the *Key Question:* "How can we build an electric motor?"
2. Distribute student pages and materials to groups.
3. Have the students make the coil by wrapping the enameled wire around a D cell five times, leaving 4 cm free at each end. Tell them to remove the D cell and twist the ends around the coil twice to hold it together. Then have them bend the ends so that they are at right angles to the coil, directly opposite each other (see illustration on student page). Direct students to scrape the insulation from the **bottom half** of these two arms (see illustration). Have them make the coil as symmetrical and well-balanced as possible.

4. Tell students to set up the motor according to the diagram on the first student page. Have them start the motor by giving the coil a spin. If the coil doesn't continue spinning, have students check the list on the second student page.
5. Challenge students to find a way to reverse the direction the coil spins or get the coil to spin faster.

Connecting Learning

1. Why does the coil spin? [Its magnetic field is repelled or attracted by the magnetic field of the ring magnets.]
2. Why must the coil be properly balanced? [An unbalanced coil does not spin as easily as a balanced one and will not keep spinning.]
3. How could you increase the speed of the motor? [increase the number of cells used and/or increase the length of wire and number of turns in your coil]
4. Where are electric motors used?
5. What are you wondering now?

Extensions

1. Take apart an old electric motor and see if you can identify its parts.
2. Have students find all the electric motors in the classroom or in their homes.

Curriculum Correlation

Social Studies
Research the history of the electric motor.

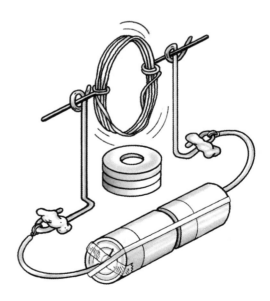

How to Make an ELECTRIC MOTOR

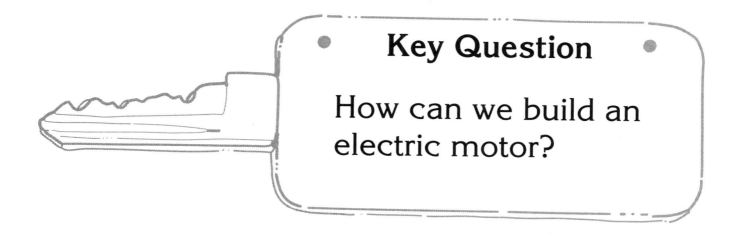

Key Question

How can we build an electric motor?

Learning Goal

build a simple electric motor.

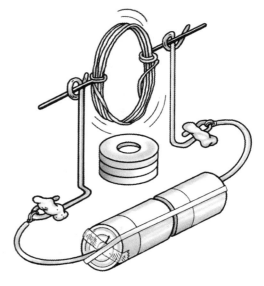

How to Make an ELECTRIC MOTOR

Materials: 2 D cells   2 jumbo paper clips   2 short wires
3 ring magnets   55 cm magnet wire   ruler and scissors
masking tape   clay

Procedure

1. Make your coil by wrapping the magnet wire tightly around a D cell. Leave 4 cm of wire free at each end. Twist these two ends around the coil twice to hold the coil together. Bend the ends away from the coil directly opposite each other as shown. Remove the D cell.

2. Use the scissors to scrape the enamel from the bottom half of each arm as shown above.

3. Bend the paper clips as shown below.

step 1   step 2

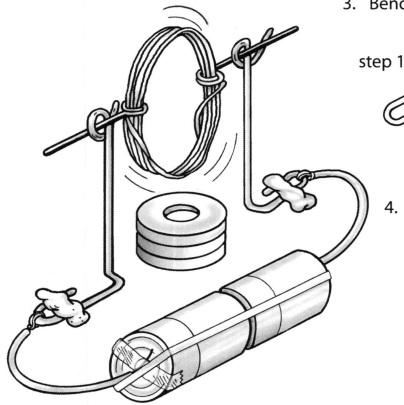

4. Set up the circuit as pictured and give the coil a spin. If it keeps going, you've built a working electric motor!

 © 2011 AIMS Education Foundation

How to Make an ELECTRIC MOTOR

If your motor does not work, check the following:

1. Your motor should be set up on a level surface.

2. Make sure your coil is as well balanced as possible. It should spin without wobbling.

3. Try spinning your coil in both directions. It may work in one direction and not the other.

4. Make sure that the wires are making good electrical contact with the battery terminals and the paper clips.

5. Try flipping the magnets over so that the opposite pole is facing the coil.

6. Make sure the enamel is completely scraped off the bottom half of each arm. The coil needs to make good electrical contact for half of each rotation.

7. Check the clearance between the bottom of the coil and the magnets. It should be about one centimeter.

8. Make sure that the two loops in the paper clips are the same height. The arms of the coil need to be level to allow the coil to spin freely. Adjust with clay.

When your motor is working, here are some challenges.

1. Make your coil spin in both directions.

2. Try to make your coil spin faster.

3. Put a switch in your circuit. It is a real challenge to get your motor to start by simply closing the switch.

© 2011 AIMS Education Foundation

How to Make an ELECTRIC MOTOR

Connecting Learning

1. Why does the coil spin?

2. Why must the coil be properly balanced?

3. How could you increase the speed of the motor?

4. Where are electric motors used?

5. What are you wondering now?

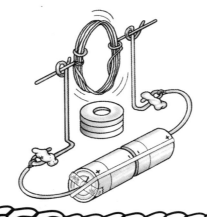

Topic
Electromagnets

Key Question
How does the number of wire wraps affect the strength of an electromagnet?

Learning Goals
Students will:
- discover how an electromagnet works,
- experiment with electromagnets by manipulating the number of wire wraps, and
- determine the relationship between the strength of the electromagnet and the number of wire wraps.

Guiding Documents
Project 2061 Benchmarks
- *Without touching them, material that has been electrically charged pulls on all other materials and may either push or pull on other charged materials.*
- *Electric currents and magnets can exert a force on each other.*
- *Find the mean of a set of data.*
- *Tables and graphs can show how values of one quantity are related to values of another.*

NRC Standards
- *Design and conduct a scientific investigation.*
- *Employ simple equipment and tools to gather data and extend the senses.*
- *Electricity in circuits can produce magnetic effects.*

NCTM Standards 2000*
- *Collect data using observations, surveys, and experiments*
- *Represent data using tables and graphs such as line plots, bar graphs, and line graphs*

Math
Data collection
Data analysis
    averages

Science
Physical science
    electromagnetism

Integrated Processes
Observing
Collecting and recording data
Identifying and controlling variables
Interpreting data

Materials
For each group:
    D cell
    battery holder
    bolts (see *Management 1*)
    insulated wire
    wire stripper
    paper clips
    student pages

Background Information
An electromagnet is a magnet that is created by the flow of electric current. A simple electromagnet is a wire connected to the terminals of a battery. The current running through the wire creates a magnetic field, and the wire acts like a magnet. When the wire is disconnected from the battery, the wire no longer acts as a magnet.

The strength of an electromagnet can be altered in a variety of ways. A coiled wire will make a stronger electromagnet than a straight wire. A coiled wire with a metal core will be stronger yet. Increasing the amount of current running through an electromagnet will also increase its strength.

This activity gives students the opportunity to explore one of the many variables affecting electromagnet strength—the number of coils, or wraps, made by the wire. Careful attention should be paid to controlling the other variables so that students' results are accurate and can be compared from group to group.

Management
1. Each group needs three bolts. The bolts must all be identical and should be at least three inches long. The core diameter does not matter as long as it is the same for all groups.
2. Students should work in groups of three or four.
3. This should not be students' first experience with electromagnets.
4. Give each group at least 25 small paper clips. If you discover that their electromagnets are able to pick up all of their paper clips, give them more.
5. Battery holders (item number 1960), bell wire (item number 1968), and wire strippers (item number 1970) are available from AIMS.

Procedure

1. Discuss with students what they have already learned about electromagnets and electromagnetism. Ask them some of the things that can affect the strength of an electromagnet. [number of coils, metal core, voltage, etc.]

2. Explain that they will be making electromagnets by wrapping wire around metal bolts. They will be testing the variable of wire wraps to see if it has any effect on the strength of an electromagnet. Ask students what kinds of things will need to be kept the same in order for this to be a fair test. [diameter and length of bolt, wire type and gauge, how the wires are wrapped, battery size, etc.]

3. Have students get into groups and distribute the student pages and the materials. Direct students' attention to the portion of the first page where it describes how to properly wrap a bolt with wire.

4. Demonstrate the procedure for students and count the number of wraps as you put on the wire. Point out how you left a tail of wire at the start and discuss how you are keeping the wire neat and the coils close together without crossing them. Explain that this is another one of the variables that students will need to control—everyone should make their coils neat and tight.

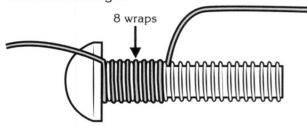

8 wraps

5. Agree as a class on three numbers of wraps to try and have students record these numbers in the appropriate spaces on the student page. (Good numbers to try are 25, 50, and 75, but students may want to do even more wraps. Discourage numbers greater than 100 because of the time and amount of wire required.) Be sure that students are aware that once they get to the end of the bolt, they will be wrapping the wire back over the top of the wires they just wrapped, and this is okay.

6. Have groups wrap their bolts the required number of times. Move from group to group and observe how neatly students are accomplishing the task. If any are being too messy, have them begin again.

7. Direct students' attention to the second page that describes how to connect the bolt to the battery holder to make the electromagnet. Remind students that they must only leave the battery in the holder for the very short periods of time when they are testing the electromagnet. If they leave the battery in the holder longer than 10 or 15 seconds at a time, the wires will get very hot and the battery will be quickly drained of all its power.

8. Allow time for groups to test their bolts five times each. Have them record the number of paper clips held each time and find the average on the third student page.

9. Conduct a time of class sharing where groups report their data. Compare results and seek reasons for any major differences. Discuss the answer to the *Key Question:* How does the number of wire wraps affect the strength of the electromagnet?

Connecting Learning

1. What things did we need to control in order to make this a fair test? [diameter and length of bolt, wire type and gauge, how the wires are wrapped, battery size, etc.]

2. Which number of wraps held the most paper clips? ...fewest?

3. How did your results compare to those of other groups? What might be some reasons for any differences?

4. Why do you think we did five trials and found the average?

5. What do your results tell us about how the number of wire wraps affects the strength of an electromagnet?

6. What other variables would you like to test? How could you design a fair test for these variables?

7. What are you wondering now?

Extensions

1. Have students list additional variables that they would like to test and design experiments to test these variables. Other things to consider include bolt diameter, bolt length, the gauge of the wire, and the voltage of the power source.

2. Have students research and/or build models of various devices that use electromagnets, such as electric motors, electrical generators, or cranes used to move scrap iron.

* Reprinted with permission from *Principles and Standards for School Mathematics*, 2000 by the National Council of Teachers of Mathematics. All rights reserved.

 © 2011 AIMS Education Foundation

ELECTROMAGNETS

Key Question

How does the number of wire wraps affect the strength of an electromagnet?

Learning Goals

Students will:

- discover how an electromagnet works,
- experiment with electromagnets by manipulating the number of wire wraps, and
- determine the relationship between the strength of the electromagnet and the number of wire wraps.

How does the number of wire wraps affect the strength of the electromagnet?

Your electromagnets will be bolts wrapped in wire, connected to D-cells. Follow these steps to make your electromagnets.

NUMBER OF WRAPS

As a class, agree on the number of wraps you will try. Record these numbers below.

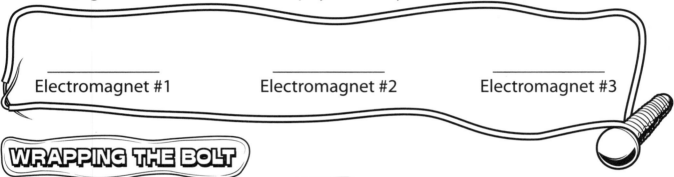

_____   _____   _____
Electromagnet #1   Electromagnet #2   Electromagnet #3

WRAPPING THE BOLT

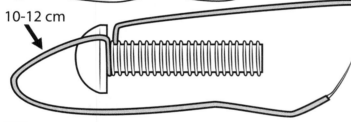

10-12 cm

1. Leave a tail of wire about 10-12 cm long. Strip the end.

2. Begin to wrap the wire at one end of the bolt.

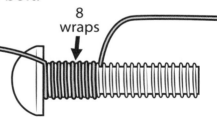

8 wraps

3. Keep the wraps tight to the bolt and close together. Do not cross them over each other. It may help to use the threads of the bolt to guide the wire.

4. Count each wrap of the wire. Every loop counts as one wrap.

5. If you get to the end of the bolt and have more wraps to do, go back over the top of the wire you already wrapped.

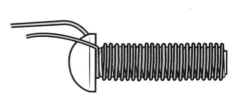

6. Once you get the desired number of wraps, cut the wire. Be sure to leave a tail that is 10-12 cm long. Strip the end.

ELECTROMAGNETS

CONNECTING THE BATTERY

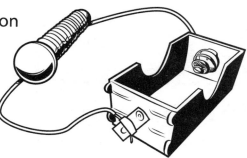

1. Put the stripped ends of the wire through the clips on the EMPTY battery holder.

2. When you are ready to test the electromagnet, put the battery in the holder. Remove the battery as soon as the electromagnet has picked up as many paper clips as it can.

CAUTION!

DO NOT leave the battery in the battery holder! This will cause the wires to get VERY hot and will quickly drain the battery of all its power.

DATA COLLECTION

1. To test your electromagnet, collect a pile of paper clips.

2. Put the battery in the battery holder and touch the electromagnet to the pile of paper clips.

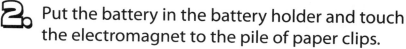

3. Lift the electromagnet up from the pile and move it to the side.

4. Remove the battery and count the number of paper clips that were stuck to the electromagnet.

5. Return the paper clips to the pile and test the same electromagnet four more times.

6. Record and graph your results on the next page.

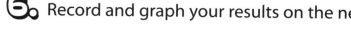

ELECTROMAGNETS

Record your results for each test and find the average for each electromagnet.

# of Wraps: _____

Trial	# of Paper Clips
1	
2	
3	
4	
5	
Average	

# of Wraps: _____

Trial	# of Paper Clips
1	
2	
3	
4	
5	
Average	

# of Wraps: _____

Trial	# of Paper Clips
1	
2	
3	
4	
5	
Average	

Make a bar graph showing the average number of paper clips held by each electromagnet. Give your graph a title and write the numbers on each axis.

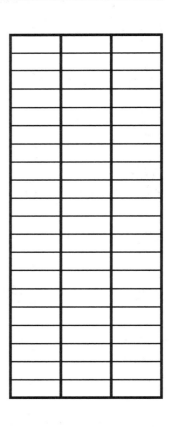

Average Number of Paper Clips

Number of Wraps

© 2011 AIMS Education Foundation

ELECTROMAGNETS

Connecting Learning

1. What things did we need to control in order to make this a fair test?

2. Which number of wraps held the most paper clips? ...fewest?

3. How did your results compare to those of other groups? What might be some reasons for any differences?

4. Why do you think we did five trials and found the average?

ELECTROMAGNETS

Connecting Learning

5. What do your results tell us about how the number of wire wraps affects the strength of an electromagnet?

6. What other variables would you like to test? How could you design a fair test for these variables?

7. What are you wondering now?

Biographies

Here are some ways to use these biography rubber band books.

1. Divide the class into three groups. Give each group the biography on one person. Have students read the factual information and create a short skit with props and narrator. Extras could include making posters to advertise the "events."

2. Let each student choose one person's biography and tell that person's story (in oral or written form) from the point of view of another person or an animal. It could even be a television (or radio) series.

3. Have students make scrapbooks containing the biography fact sheets plus other reports and clippings related to the person or persons chosen.

4. Each student might choose one inventor, research that person, and make other pictures with captions besides those provided.

5. Discuss the impact of the inventions of these three people. Take a class or school survey to determine what students think are the major inventions during all time or during any given time period like the twentieth century.

6. Research other inventors, especially women and those of under-represented groups.

7. Challenge students to go through one day without using something one of these three men invented or improved upon.

ELECTRICAL CONNECTIONS

195

© 2011 AIMS Education Foundation

When Edison was 12, he took a job selling newspapers on board the Grand Trunk Railway. In his spare time, he would do experiments in the baggage car. One day, an experiment caught fire. He was kicked off the train, chemicals and all.

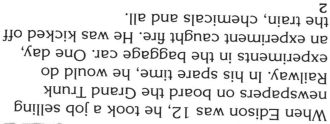

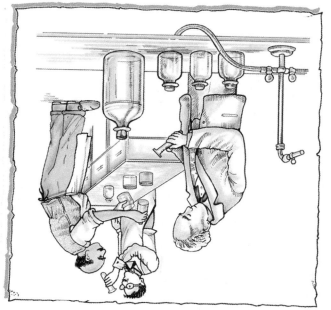

Even after he was 80 years old, Edison was busy creating and improving inventions. He began research on synthetic rubber. In 1931, while working in his laboratory, he collapsed and died.

Thomas Edison was one of the greatest inventors in the history of our country. He patented over 1000 inventions in his lifetime. He has become known worldwide as the "Wizard of Menlo Park."

8

Thomas Edison

Thomas Edison was born in Ohio on February 11, 1847. He began school at the age of seven. His schooling lasted only three months because his teachers were angry that he asked too many unusual questions. From then on, Edison's mother, a teacher, taught him at home.

1

© 2011 AIMS Education Foundation

His favorite invention was the phonograph. He invented it in 1877. The first words ever recorded on the machine were, "Mary had a little lamb."

In addition to his own inventions, including a vote-counting machine, he improved upon the inventions of others: the telegraph, the typewriter, and stock ticker systems.

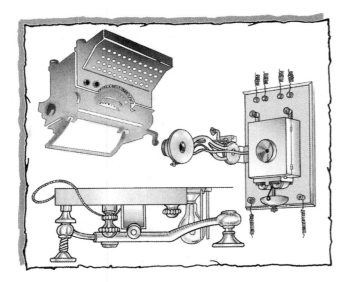

Edison was nearly deaf. He believed that he lost his hearing when a well-meaning conductor tried to help him board a moving train by pulling him by his ears. Edison could have had an operation to cure his deafness, but he did not want to because he found it easier to concentrate when it was quiet.

In 1879, while living in Menlo Park, New Jersey, Edison worked on perfecting the electric light. He spent two years searching for the proper filament. Finally, after over 7000 tries, he successfully invented the electric light bulb.

Franklin is the only American to have signed all four major documents of his time: the Declaration of Independence, the Constitution, the Treaty of Alliance with France, and the Treaty of Peace with Great Britain.

At 12, he became an apprentice printer. This led to printing a newspaper, the paper currency for several colonies, and *Poor Richard's Almanac*, which is a collection of wise sayings.

Benjamin Franklin was a talented man. He served his nation as a statesman, scientist, and community servant.

Benjamin Franklin was born on January 17, 1706. He was the 10th son of 17 children. His father was a soapmaker and a candlemaker.

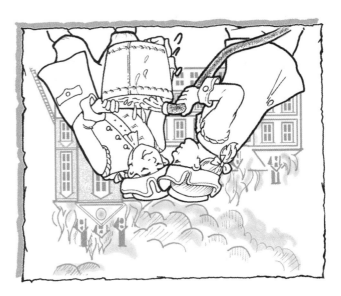

He brought about many improvements in Philadelphia. Alarmed by the large number of homes and businesses lost to fire, Franklin established a volunteer fire department. He also organized the first hospital in America.

He made a kite that he flew during a thunderstorm. Lightning struck a wire on the kite. Static electricity traveled down the string and caused a spark on the key. This experiment led to the invention of the lightning rod and proved that lightning is actually electricity.

His love of books led him to create the first subscription library in America. Members contributed money that was used to purchase books. These books were then loaned to the members free of charge. It allowed people access to many books.

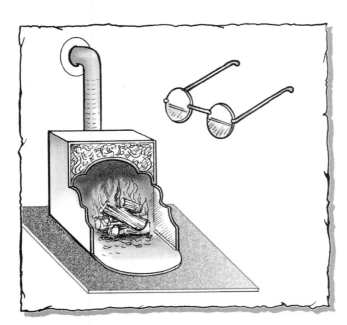

Other inventions included bifocal glasses and the Franklin stove. Since people used stoves for heating their homes, it was important that the Franklin stove gave off more heat than regular stoves.

Humanoid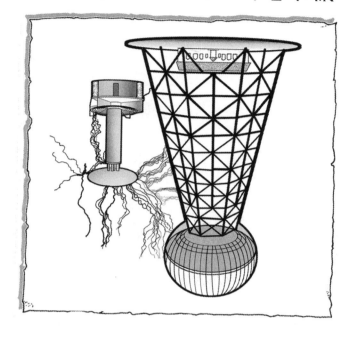

Nikola Tesla made many contributions to a wide variety of scientific fields in his life. He died in his New York City hotel room on January 7, 1943 at the age of 86.

Tesla went to the Higher Real Gymnasium in Karlovac, where he completed a four-year course in only three years. He then went to the Gratz University of Technology, where he studied electrical engineering before leaving in 1878 without a degree.

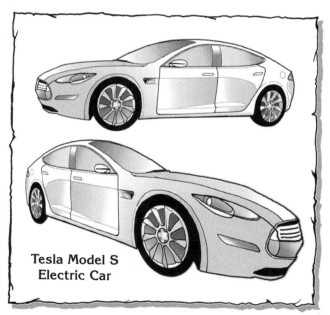

Tesla Model S Electric Car

Tesla has been honored in many ways since his death. The unit for measuring magnetic fields is called a tesla. There is a crater on the far side of the moon named Tesla in his honor. There is even a company that makes electric cars named Tesla Motors.

8

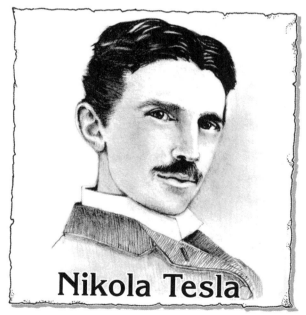

Nikola Tesla

Nikola Tesla was an inventor and engineer whose ideas and inventions led to our modern alternating current (AC) power system. He was born on July 10, 1856 in Smiljan in what is now Croatia. He was the fourth of five children.

1

There was a long and nasty battle over which kind of system was best. It has been called "The War of the Currents." In the end, Tesla's AC system won out, and that is the kind of current we use today in our homes and businesses.

In 1888, he began working with George Westinghouse on a system for using alternating current (AC) to transmit electricity over long distances. All of the electricity in the United States at the time was direct current (DC). This was the system developed by Thomas Edison.

Alternator

Tesla was a unique and unusual man. He claimed to have a photographic memory. He also had visions in which he would see solutions to problems or picture inventions in detail before they were created.

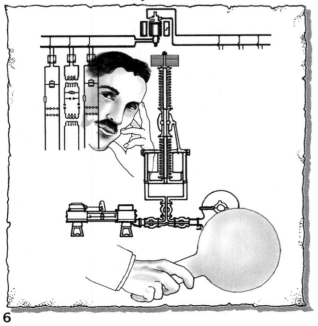

Welcome to the United States

He moved and traveled for several years, finally coming to America in 1884. He began working for Thomas Edison and helped improve Edison's motor and generators. Edison reportedly promised to pay him $50,000 for this work. When Edison broke his word and did not pay up, Tesla resigned.

© 2011 AIMS Education Foundation

Topic
History of electricity

Key Question
How did discoveries about electricity develop over a period of time?

Learning Goal
Students will construct a time line of some major events in the history of electricity.

Guiding Documents
Project 2061 Benchmarks
- *The human ability to shape the future comes from a capacity for generating knowledge and developing new technologies—and communicating ideas to others.*
- *Technology has strongly influenced the course of history and continues to do so.*

NRC Standards
- *Science and technology have been practiced by people for a long time.*
- *Men and women have made a variety of contributions throughout the history of science and technology.*

Math
Sequencing
Measurement
Estimation

Science
Physical science
    electricity
        history

Integrated Processes
Observing
Comparing and contrasting
Classifying
Collecting data
Organizing data

Materials
For each group of four:
    one copy of date page
    three copies of inventor page
    clear tape
    crayons
    scissors
    one 2-3 m piece of yarn
    meter stick or tape, optional

For each student:
    Charging in Time fact sheets

Background Information
See *Charging In Time* fact sheets.

Management
1. Students should work in groups of four.
2. Hang the long piece of yarn near where each group will meet. Older students can measure the total length and divide by the number of dates.
3. Each student will need three *Inventor* cards. There are four on the page in case students want to make a revision.

Procedure
1. Tell students that they are going to construct a time line that will show the dates of some electrical inventions and discoveries.
2. Put students in groups of four. Invite them to read the *Charging in Time* fact sheets.
3. Tell students that each group member will select three of the inventions or discoveries listed on the fact sheets, summarize the information, and draw the inventions on the *Inventor* cards.
4. Distribute a copy of the date page to each group. Have students cut along the solid lines and fold each piece along the dashed line. Have students put the dates on the yarn so that they are equally spaced (they can use a meter stick/tape to do this) and tape or staple them in place.
5. Have each group hang their invention summary cards (using the short pieces of yarn) on their time lines. Students should place the cards in the correct position by interpolating (estimating the distance between two points). For example, a card about Oersted's 1820 discovery of the relationship between electricity and magnetism would be placed between the 1800 and 1825 dates on the time line, but it would be much closer to 1825.

6. Have each group study their completed time line and interpret the data.
7. As a class, discuss the importance of various inventions.

Connecting Learning
1. What information do you get from the time line?
2. How is this information similar to the information on the fact sheet?
3. How is this information different from the fact sheet?
4. What are some advantages of presenting this kind of information in the form of a time line?
5. What are the disadvantages?
6. Which period had the most inventions?
7. Why do you think that happened?
8. What are you wondering now?

Extensions
1. Research other electrical inventions/discoveries and add them to the time line.
2. Make a time line that starts in more modern times and focuses on modern inventions that use electricity such as the VCR, CD and DVD players, fax machines, etc.
3. Make time lines for other areas of study.

Curriculum Correlation
Language Arts
Write a news article or advertisement for one of the inventions on the time line.

Social Studies
Find out more about some of the scientists or inventions of the time line.

ELECTRICAL CONNECTIONS   204   © 2011 AIMS Education Foundation

Electricity Time Line

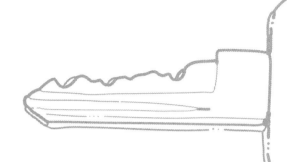

Key Question

How did discoveries about electricity develop over a period of time?

Learning Goal

Students will:

construct a time line of some major events in the history of electricity.

Date

Inventor

Invention

Date

Inventor

Invention

Date

Inventor

Invention

Date

Inventor

Invention

1750	1750	1925	1925
1775	1775	1900	1900
1800	1800	1875	1875
1825	1825	1850	1850

Charging in Time

Many people have contributed to our understanding of electricity today. The ancient Greeks discovered that amber rubbed with cloth would attract bits of straw and other light objects. This phenomenon, which was caused by static electricity, was known for over 2000 years before it was studied in any great depth. In the early 1600s, William Gilbert, a physicist from England, was the first to study static electricity in a scientific way. He is credited with coining the word *electricity*, which comes from the Greek word for amber. It was more than 100 years before research on electricity progressed much farther.

In the summer of 1752, Benjamin Franklin performed his famous kite experiment that proved that lightning was an electric phenomenon. Franklin was lucky not to have been killed, a fate that fell on some who tried to duplicate his experiment. That same year he made the first lightning rod and placed it on the top of a house. When the lightning struck, it hit the rod and was short-circuited to the ground, sparing the house.

In 1800, Alessandro Volta of Italy made the first wet-cell battery that produced an electrical current. He placed zinc and silver discs in an acid solution and an electric current flowed through a wire that was connected to the discs.

In 1820, Hans Oersted from Denmark discovered the connection between electricity and magnetism. He noticed that an electric current in a wire deflected a compass needle that was nearby. He discovered that whenever an electric current flows through a wire, a magnetic field is created. Oersted's discovery led John Schweigger to invent the first galvanometer, a device to detect electric currents, in 1821.

© 2011 AIMS Education Foundation

Also in 1821, Michael Faraday from Great Britain invented the first basic electric motor. He placed a wire carrying an electric current between the poles of a magnet. When the two magnetic fields met, they caused a force that made the wire turn around, creating the first electric motor.

In 1823 W. Sturgeon, a scientist from Great Britain, made the first electromagnet by passing an electric current through a wire that was wrapped around an iron bar. The iron bar became a powerful magnet when an electric current was going through the wires wrapped around it.

Michael Faraday invented the first transformer in 1831. This device could change the voltage of an electric current. When a current with a low voltage entered the transformer, it was transformed into a current with a higher voltage coming out.

In 1844, Samuel Morse successfully transmitted a message by magnetic telegraph. This invention allowed people to communicate over great distances.

A Frenchman, G. Leclanche, made the first dry-cell battery in 1866 by combining different chemicals in a small round container. The dry-cell battery made it possible to have a convenient, easy-to-use source of power.

For the next few years, Thomas Edison was very busy inventing many different products. In 1877, he developed the first phonograph. Two years later, in 1879, he invented the first successful electric light bulb. It was a glass bulb that burned for only 13 1/2 hours. Luckily, a year before in 1878, J. Swan had developed a vacuum pump to remove the air from a bulb so the filament would not burn away.

In 1907, the electric vacuum cleaner and washing machine were invented. These made household chores much easier.

It wasn't until 1910 that G. Claude produced the first neon light. This Frenchman passed an electric current through a neon gas tube that made the gas glow red.

In 1925, J. Baird from Scotland demonstrated the first television set. It was many years later before it became available to many families.

Connecting Learning

1. What information do you get from the time line?

2. How is this information similar to the information on the fact sheet?

3. How is this information different from the fact sheet?

4. What are some advantages of presenting this kind of information in the form of a time line?

ELECTRICAL CONNECTIONS

© 2011 AIMS Education Foundation

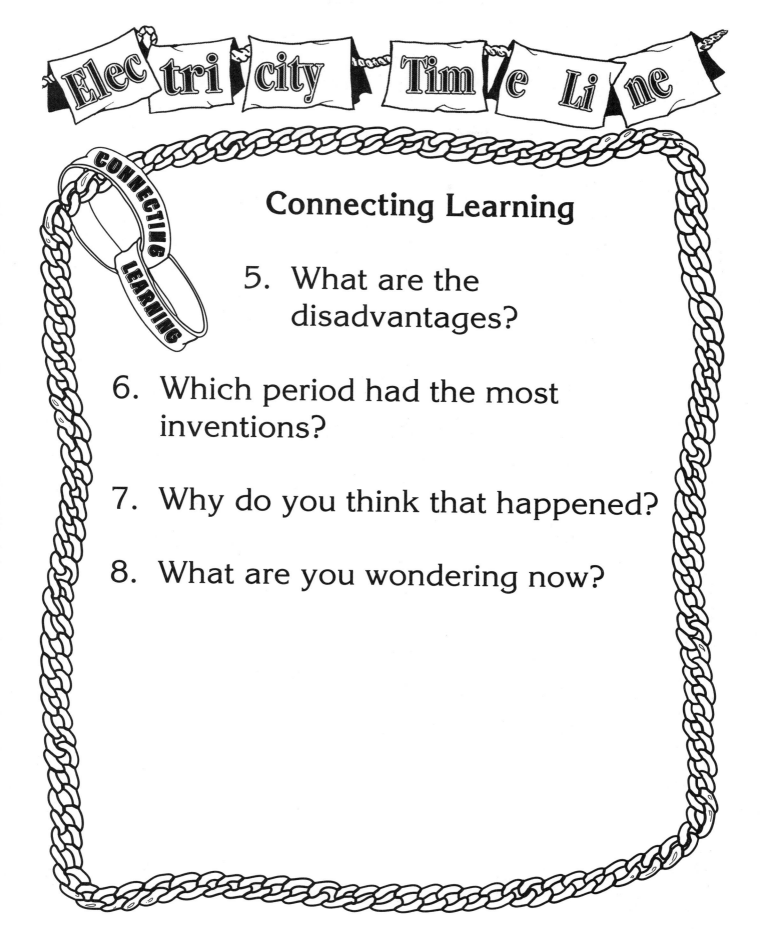

Electricity Time Line

Connecting Learning

5. What are the disadvantages?

6. Which period had the most inventions?

7. Why do you think that happened?

8. What are you wondering now?

 © 2011 AIMS Education Foundation

WHEN I WAS TEN

Topic
History of electricity

Key Question
How have electrical inventions changed the way we live?

Learning Goal
Students will find out how daily living and the uses of electricity have changed through the years by interviewing older people.

Guiding Documents
Project 2061 Benchmark
- *Technology has strongly influenced the course of history and continues to do so.*

NRC Standards
- *Science and technology have been practiced by people for a long time.*
- *Men and women have made a variety of contributions throughout the history of science and technology.*

Math
Sequencing
Calculating age

Science
Electricity
   history

Integrated Processes
Classifying
Organizing data
Reporting

Materials
Student pages

Background Information
Students (and adults) take the conveniences of modern life for granted. They do not stop to think that things like TVs, refrigerators, or computers have not always been available and that their grandparents or other older people actually went through childhood without these "necessities." This activity is designed to help students realize what important changes have come about through the use of devices that use electricity.

Management
1. This activity has three parts. *Part One* includes a class discussion and an assignment for students to interview older people in their families or neighborhoods. *Part Two* is done after students have completed their interviews, perhaps several days later. *Part Three* enables students to calculate someone's age.
2. If most students do not have access to older people in their families or neighborhoods, adapt the activity by conducting interviews on the phone. Seniors might enjoy visiting the school to be interviewed. Planning the activity just before Thanksgiving or another family-oriented holiday might also help.
3. This activity is designed to focus on how life has changed because of modern electrical conveniences, but it certainly should not be limited to this focus. It might be good for today's students to hear seniors talk about how they spent their time as school-age children.

Procedure
Part One
1. Introduce the lesson by brainstorming activities students like. After a list has been generated, discuss which activities are directly or indirectly related to electricity. Many activities will be linked directly to electricity: watching television, listening to music, playing video games, etc. Others will be linked less directly: playing baseball involves the use of bats, balls, and gloves made in factories using electricity. Through this discussion, students will become aware of the many ways electricity and electrical devices affect their lives.
2. Discuss the *Key Question*: "How have electrical inventions changed the way we live?" Ask students to imagine what life would be like without some of the modern conveniences like TVs, vacuum cleaners, telephones, etc.
3. Ask students how they think their great-grandparents or grandparents performed simple tasks like cleaning their house or cooking their food when they were 10. Ask students what they think their grandparents did for entertainment when they were young and how it was different from what school-age children do today. Tell the class that they will try to find the answers to these and other questions by interviewing older people.

4. Distribute an interview sheet to each student. Tell students that you would like them to interview a grandparent, great-grandparent, or other senior. The interviews will focus on what their lives were like when they were 10.

5. Tell students that the questions listed on the interview sheet are to help them get started with their interviews. Encourage them to add questions of their own in the spaces provided. The back of the sheet can be used for information volunteered by the person interviewed or for additional questions.

6. Give the students a deadline for getting the interviews completed.

Part Two
1. After students have finished the interview process, have them share their findings.
2. Discuss some of the ways that the life of a 10-year-old was different in the childhood of the person interviewed.
3. Brainstorm a list of common electrical devices that were not available when the people interviewed were younger.
4. Discuss the differences these devices have made in our lifestyles.
5. Have students try to imagine living in a world without modern electrical conveniences.
6. Have students pick three electric devices and write what they would use if they didn't have that device.
7. Have students write a paragraph describing how their lives would be different without electricity.

Part Three
1. Have them calculate their age and date of birth using the steps outlined.
2. Have students calculate the age of their senior friend using the information from the interview.

Connecting Learning
1. How have electrical devices changed the way we live?
2. Are all of these changes for the better? Explain.
3. Would you have liked to have been a child during the time your grandparents were growing up? Why or why not?
4. What electrical devices do you feel you could live without?
5. What electrical devices do you feel you couldn't live without?
6. What are you wondering now?

Extensions
1. Make a time line that shows some of the major electrical inventions from the time your grandparents were 10 up to the present.
2. Find some inventions that are less than 10 years old and learn more about them.
3. Try to imagine how your life will be different in 50 years because of new inventions and write about it.

Curriculum Correlation
Language Arts
Write a story about the childhood of your grandparents or whomever you interviewed.

Art
Make a collage that shows modern electrical devices. Draw pictures of what you think your home will look like in 50 years.

Literature
Have students read the series of four chapter books by Jeanne DuPrau:
The City of Ember, The People of Sparks, The Prophet of Yonwood, and *The Diamond of Darkhold.*
The series begins with the people of Ember who have lived underground for 250 years. Their livelihood is threatened when their antiquated generator begins to fail. Implications of the loss of electricity will cause readers to consider their own electrical dependencies.

Home Link
Challenge students (and parents) to do without TV for one full day. Discuss the reactions in the students' homes.

WHEN I WAS TEN

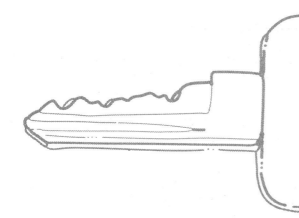

Key Question

How have electrical inventions changed the way we live?

Learning Goal

Students will:

find out how daily living and the uses of electricity have changed through the years by interviewing older people.

WHEN I WAS TEN
Part One

Our class at school is studying electricity. We are trying to find out what difference electricity has made in people's lives. We appreciate your willingness to help us.

1. What is your name?

2. When you were 10 years old, did your home have electricity?

3. What is your date of birth?   year_____month_____day_____

4. Did you have a television set growing up? Was its picture color or black and white?

5. What changes have you experienced with how you listen to music?

6. What kitchen appliances do you have now that you didn't have when you were 10?

7. How has the use of electricity improved your life?

Thank your for talking with me.

_____Interviewer

WHEN I WAS TEN
Part Two

Electricity is part of our lives. Although it is difficult to imagine what life would be like without our things that use electricity, let's think what we would do instead.

If I didn't have…

I would…

If I didn't have…

I would…

If I didn't have…

I would…

Describe what you think your life would have been like without electricity.

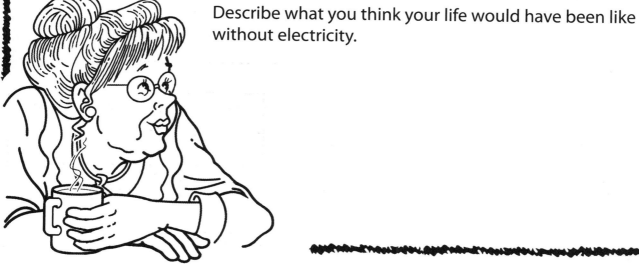

217

© 2011 AIMS Education Foundation

WHEN I WAS TEN

Part Three

Here's how to find out how old someone is when you know the date of birth. Try it first with your own birth date.

1. Fill in today's date and your date of birth in the table.
2. Subtract the days first.
   (If you need to regroup, change 1 month to 30 days.)
3. Next, subtract the months.
   (If you need to regroup, change 1 year to 12 months.)
4. Then, subtract the years.
5. You now have your age: _____ years, _____ months, and _____ days.

	Year	Month	Day
Today's Date			
Your Birthdate			
Your Age			

If you know a person's age, here is how to find out when a person was born. Again, try it with your own.

1. Fill in today's date and your age in the table.
2. Subtract the days first.

	Year	Month	Day
Today's Date			
Your Age			
Your Birthdate			

3. This is the date of birth _____ year, _____ month, and _____ day.

Now find our your senior friend's age.

1. Fill in today's date and his or her date of birth in the table.
2. Subtract.

	Year	Month	Day
Today's Date			
Your Friend's Birthdate			
Your Friend's Age			

3. The person's age is: _____ years, _____ months, and _____ days.

218 © 2011 AIMS Education Foundation

WHEN I WAS TEN

Connecting Learning

1. How have electrical devices changed the way we live?

2. Are all of these changes for the better? Explain.

3. Would you have liked to have been a child during the time your grandparents were growing up? Why or why not?

4. What electrical devices do you feel you could live without?

5. What electrical devices do you feel you couldn't live without?

6. What are you wondering now?

 © 2011 AIMS Education Foundation

Problem-Solving Activities for Challenge and Assessment

The activities in this book are designed to be self-assessing. For example, you can tell whether or not students can build a circuit by having them do it. At the end of an electricity unit, however, you may wish to use different activities to see if students can apply what they have learned. You may also wish to provide them with challenges to stimulate further growth and creative thinking. If you use these activities for performance-based assessment, be sure all students being assessed have done successfully the investigations on which these activities are based.

1. Make a working flashlight using a toilet paper tube, a three-ounce paper cup, some aluminum foil, a flashlight bulb, and a D cell. The flashlight should have a switch.

2. Make a model of a village using boxes and construction paper. Install circuits and lights in each of the buildings in the village.

3. Devise a play in which students model what happens in an electric circuit. Students play the part of switches, lights, batteries, fuses, and electric charges (electrons).

4. Make a test circuit containing a light bulb to test the conductivity of different liquids. Some suggested liquids to test are salt water, vinegar, sugar water, and lemon juice.

5. Make a model of a fuse by taping a single strand of steel wool to a piece of tag board. Put the fuse in a circuit and vary the number of cells used to power the circuit. Try to make a fuse that will not burn with one or two cells in the circuit, but will burn with three cells.

CRACKLE

 © 2011 AIMS Education Foundation

Electrical Connections

Materials

Equipment

*Battery holders (1960)
*Bulb holders (1958)
*Bulbs (1926)
*Insulated wire (1968)
*Magnet wire (1967)
*Wire strippers (1970)
*Ring magnets (1971)

*Metric rulers (1909)
*Directional compasses (1990)
28-gauge wire
20-gauge copper wire
Alligator clips
Incandescent light bulb
Fluorescent light bulb

Consumables and Non-consumables

#2 pencils
Pencil shavings
Crayons
#19 rubber bands
Heavy-duty rubber bands
Small paper clips
Jumbo paper clips
Paper fasteners
Transparent tape
Masking tape
Glue sticks
Scissors
Hole punch
Stapler
Index cards, 5" x 7"
Index cards, 3" x 5"
Cardboard, 6-cm squares

Plastic wrap
Aluminum foil
Paper towels
Steel wool
Baby food jars
Yarn
Thread
Clay
Rubber balloons
Colored buttons or plastic chips
D cells
6-volt lantern battery
Clock that ticks
Nails—10 penny, 8 d
Metal washers, 3/8-inch diameter
Bolts
Salt

*Available from AIMS

 © 2011 AIMS Education Foundation

The AIMS Program

AIMS is the acronym for "**A**ctivities **I**ntegrating **M**athematics and **S**cience." Such integration enriches learning and makes it meaningful and holistic. AIMS began as a project of Fresno Pacific University to integrate the study of mathematics and science in grades K-9, but has since expanded to include language arts, social studies, and other disciplines.

AIMS is a continuing program of the non-profit AIMS Education Foundation. It had its inception in a National Science Foundation funded program whose purpose was to explore the effectiveness of integrating mathematics and science. The project directors in cooperation with 80 elementary classroom teachers devoted two years to a thorough field-testing of the results and implications of integration.

The approach met with such positive results that the decision was made to launch a program to create instructional materials incorporating this concept. Despite the fact that thoughtful educators have long recommended an integrative approach, very little appropriate material was available in 1981 when the project began. A series of writing projects ensued, and today the AIMS Education Foundation is committed to continuing the creation of new integrated activities on a permanent basis.

The AIMS program is funded through the sale of books, products, and staff development workshops, and through proceeds from the Foundation's endowment. All net income from programs and products flows into a trust fund administered by the AIMS Education Foundation. Use of these funds is restricted to support of research, development, and publication of new materials. Writers donate all their rights to the Foundation to support its on-going program. No royalties are paid to the writers.

The rationale for integration lies in the fact that science, mathematics, language arts, social studies, etc., are integrally interwoven in the real world, from which it follows that they should be similarly treated in the classroom where students are being prepared to live in that world. Teachers who use the AIMS program give enthusiastic endorsement to the effectiveness of this approach.

Science encompasses the art of questioning, investigating, hypothesizing, discovering, and communicating. Mathematics is a language that provides clarity, objectivity, and understanding. The language arts provide us with powerful tools of communication. Many of the major contemporary societal issues stem from advancements in science and must be studied in the context of the social sciences. Therefore, it is timely that all of us take seriously a more holistic method of educating our students. This goal motivates all who are associated with the AIMS Program. We invite you to join us in this effort.

Meaningful integration of knowledge is a major recommendation coming from the nation's professional science and mathematics associations. The American Association for the Advancement of Science in *Science for All Americans* strongly recommends the integration of mathematics, science, and technology. The National Council of Teachers of Mathematics places strong emphasis on applications of mathematics found in science investigations. AIMS is fully aligned with these recommendations.

Extensive field testing of AIMS investigations confirms these beneficial results:

1. Mathematics becomes more meaningful, hence more useful, when it is applied to situations that interest students.
2. The extent to which science is studied and understood is increased when mathematics and science are integrated.
3. There is improved quality of learning and retention, supporting the thesis that learning which is meaningful and relevant is more effective.
4. Motivation and involvement are increased dramatically as students investigate real-world situations and participate actively in the process.

We invite you to become part of this classroom teacher movement by using an integrated approach to learning and sharing any suggestions you may have. The AIMS Program welcomes you!

© 2011 AIMS Education Foundation

AIMS Education Foundation Programs

When you host an AIMS workshop for elementary and middle school educators, you will know your teachers are receiving effective, usable training they can apply in their classrooms immediately.

AIMS Workshops are Designed for Teachers

- Correlated to your state standards;
- Address key topic areas, including math content, science content, and process skills;
- Provide practice of activity-based teaching;
- Address classroom management issues and higher-order thinking skills;
- Give you AIMS resources; and
- Offer optional college (graduate-level) credits for many courses.

AIMS Workshops Fit District/Administrative Needs

- Flexible scheduling and grade-span options;
- Customized (one-, two-, or three-day) workshops meet specific schedule, topic, state standards, and grade-span needs;
- Prepackaged four-day workshops for in-depth math and science training available (includes all materials and expenses);
- Sustained staff development is available for which workshops can be scheduled throughout the school year;
- Eligible for funding under the Title I and Title II sections of No Child Left Behind; and
- Affordable professional development—consecutive-day workshops offer considerable savings.

University Credit—Correspondence Courses

AIMS offers correspondence courses through a partnership with Fresno Pacific University.

- Convenient distance-learning courses—you study at your own pace and schedule. No computer or Internet access required!

Introducing AIMS State-Specific Science Curriculum

Developed to meet 100% of your state's standards, AIMS' State-Specific Science Curriculum gives students the opportunity to build content knowledge, thinking skills, and fundamental science processes.

- Each grade-specific module has been developed to extend the AIMS approach to full-year science programs. Modules can be used as a complete curriculum or as a supplement to existing materials.
- Each standards-based module includes math, reading, hands-on investigations, and assessments.

Like all AIMS resources, these modules are able to serve students at all stages of readiness, making these a great value across the grades served in your school.

For current information regarding the programs described above, please complete the following form and mail it to: P.O. Box 8120, Fresno, CA 93747.

Information Request

Please send current information on the items checked:

____ *Basic Information Packet* on AIMS materials

____ Hosting information for AIMS workshops

____ AIMS State-Specific Science Curriculum

Name: _____

Phone:_____E-mail:_____

Address: _____
Street   City   State   Zip

© 2011 AIMS Education Foundation

AIMS™ Magazine

Your K-9 Math and Science Classroom Activities Resource

The AIMS Magazine is your source for standards-based, hands-on math and science investigations. Each issue is filled with teacher-friendly, ready-to-use activities that engage students in meaningful learning.

• *Four issues each year (fall, winter, spring, and summer).*

Current issue is shipped with all past issues within that volume.

| 1824 | Volume | XXV | 2010-2011 | $19.95 |
| 1825 | Volume | XXVI | 2011-2012 | $19.95 |

Two-Volume Combinations

| M21012 | Volumes | XXV & XXVI | 2010-12 | $34.95 |
| M21113 | Volumes | XXVI & XXVII | 2011-13 | $34.95 |

Complete volumes available for purchase:

| 1823 | Volume | XXIII | 2008-2009 | $19.95 |
| 1824 | Volume | XXIV | 2009-2010 | $19.95 |

AIMS Online—www.aimsedu.org

To see all that AIMS has to offer, check us out on the Internet at www.aimsedu.org. At our website you can preview and purchase AIMS books and individual activities, learn about State-Specific Science and Essential Math, explore professional development workshops and online learning opportunities, search our activities database, buy manipulatives and other classroom resources, and download free resources including articles, puzzles, and sample AIMS activities.

AIMS E-mail Specials

While visiting the AIMS website, sign up for our FREE e-mail newsletter with monthly subscriber-only specials. You'll also receive advance notice of new products.

Sign up today!

Subscribe to the **AIMS** Magazine

$19.95 a year!

AIMS Magazine is published four times a year.

Subscriptions ordered at any time will receive all issues for that year.

Call **1.888.733.2467** or go to **www.aimsedu.org**

© 2011 AIMS Education Foundation

AIMS Program Publications

Actions With Fractions, 4-9
The Amazing Circle, 4-9
Awesome Addition and Super Subtraction, 2-3
Bats Incredible! 2-4
Brick Layers II, 4-9
The Budding Botanist, 3-6
Chemistry Matters, 5-7
Counting on Coins, K-2
Cycles of Knowing and Growing, 1-3
Crazy About Cotton, 3-7
Critters, 2-5
Earth Book, 6-9
Electrical Connections, 4-6
Energy Explorations: Sound, Light, and Heat, 3-5
Exploring Environments, K-6
Fabulous Fractions, 3-6
Fall Into Math and Science*, K-1
Field Detectives, 3-6
Finding Your Bearings, 4-9
Floaters and Sinkers, 5-9
From Head to Toe, 5-9
Getting Into Geometry, K-1
Glide Into Winter With Math and Science*, K-1
Gravity Rules! 5-12
Hardhatting in a Geo-World, 3-5
Historical Connections in Mathematics, Vol. I, 5-9
Historical Connections in Mathematics, Vol. II, 5-9
Historical Connections in Mathematics, Vol. III, 5-9
It's About Time, K-2
It Must Be A Bird, Pre-K-2
Jaw Breakers and Heart Thumpers, 3-5
Looking at Geometry, 6-9
Looking at Lines, 6-9
Machine Shop, 5-9
Magnificent Microworld Adventures, 6-9
Marvelous Multiplication and Dazzling Division, 4-5
Math + Science, A Solution, 5-9
Mathematicians are People, Too
Mathematicians are People, Too, Vol. II
Mostly Magnets, 3-6
Movie Math Mania, 6-9
Multiplication the Algebra Way, 6-8
Out of This World, 4-8
Paper Square Geometry:
    The Mathematics of Origami, 5-12
Puzzle Play, 4-8

Popping With Power, 3-5
Positive vs. Negative, 6-9
Primarily Bears*, K-6
Primarily Magnets, K-2
Primarily Physics: Investigations in Sound, Light,
    and Heat Energy, K-2
Primarily Plants, K-3
Primarily Weather, K-3
Problem Solving: Just for the Fun of It! 4-9
Problem Solving: Just for the Fun of It! Book Two, 4-9
Proportional Reasoning, 6-9
Ray's Reflections, 4-8
Sensational Springtime, K-2
Sense-able Science, K-1
Shapes, Solids, and More: Concepts in Geometry, 2-3
The Sky's the Limit, 5-9
Soap Films and Bubbles, 4-9
Solve It! K-1: Problem-Solving Strategies, K-1
Solve It! 2nd: Problem-Solving Strategies, 2
Solve It! 3rd: Problem-Solving Strategies, 3
Solve It! 4th: Problem-Solving Strategies, 4
Solve It! 5th: Problem-Solving Strategies, 5
Solving Equations: A Conceptual Approach, 6-9
Spatial Visualization, 4-9
Spills and Ripples, 5-12
Spring Into Math and Science*, K-1
Statistics and Probability, 6-9
Through the Eyes of the Explorers, 5-9
Under Construction, K-2
Water, Precious Water, 4-6
Weather Sense: Temperature, Air Pressure, and Wind, 4-5
Weather Sense: Moisture, 4-5
What's Next, Volume 1, 4-12
What's Next, Volume 2, 4-12
What's Next, Volume 3, 4-12
Winter Wonders, K-2

Essential Math
Area Formulas for Parallelograms, Triangles, and Trapezoids, 6-8
Circumference and Area of Circles, 5-7
Effects of Changing Lengths, 6-8
Measurement of Prisms, Pyramids, Cylinders, and Cones, 6-8
Measurement of Rectangular Solids, 5-7
Perimeter and Area of Rectangles, 4-6
The Pythagorean Relationship, 6-8

Spanish Edition
Constructores II: Ingeniería Creativa Con Construcciones
    LEGO®, 4-9
    The entire book is written in Spanish. English pages not included.

* Spanish supplements are available for these books. They are only
    available as downloads from the AIMS website. The supplements
    contain only the student pages in Spanish; you will need the English
    version of the book for the teacher's text.

For further information, contact:
AIMS Education Foundation • P.O. Box 8120 • Fresno, California 93747-8120
www.aimsedu.org • 559.255.6396 (fax) • 888.733.2467 (toll free)

© 2011 AIMS Education Foundation

Duplication Rights

No part of any AIMS books, magazines, activities, or content—digital or otherwise—may be reproduced or transmitted in any form or by any means—including photocopying, scanning, taping, or information storage/retrieval systems—except as noted below.

Standard Duplication Rights

- A person or school purchasing AIMS activities (in books, magazines, or in digital form) is hereby granted permission to make up to 200 copies of any portion of those activities, provided these copies will be used for educational purposes and only at one school site.
- For a workshop or conference session, presenters may make one copy of any portion of a purchased activity for each participant, with a limit of five activities or up to one-third of a book, whichever is less.
- All copies must bear the AIMS Education Foundation copyright information.
- Modifications to AIMS pages (e.g., separating page elements for use on an interactive white board) are permitted only within the classroom or school for which they were purchased, or by presenters at conferences or workshops. Interactive white board files may not be uploaded to any third-party website or otherwise distributed. AIMS artwork and content may not be used on non-AIMS materials.

Standard duplication rights apply to activities received at workshops, free sample activities provided by AIMS, and activities received by conference participants.

Unlimited Duplication Rights

Unlimited duplication rights may be purchased in cases where AIMS users wish to:
- make more than 200 copies of a book/magazine/activity,
- use a book/magazine/activity at more than one school site, or
- make an activity available on the Internet (see below).

These rights permit unlimited duplication of purchased books, magazines, and/or activities (including revisions) for use at a given school site.

Activities received at workshops are eligible for upgrade from standard to unlimited duplication rights.

Free sample activities and activities received as a conference participant are not eligible for upgrade from standard to unlimited duplication rights.

State-Specific Science modules are licensed to one classroom/one teacher and are therefore not eligible for upgrade from standard to unlimited duplication rights.

Upgrade Fees

The fees for upgrading from standard to unlimited duplication rights are as follows.
For individual activities, the cost is $5 per activity per school site.
For books, the cost is based on the price of the book (see table).

Book Price	Upgrade Fee
$9.95	$15.00/site
$18.95	$24.00/site
$21.95	$27.00/site
$24.95	$30.00/site
$34.95	$40.00/site
$49.95	$55.00/site

The cost of upgrading is shown in the following examples:
For five activities at six schools:
 5 activities x $5 x 6 schools = $150

For two books (at $21.95) at 10 schools:
 2 books x $27 x 10 schools = $540

For three books (at $24.95) and four activities at eight schools:
 (3 books x $30 x 8 schools) + (4 activites x $5 x 8 schools) = $720 + $160 = $880

Purchasing Unlimited Duplication Rights

To purchase unlimited duplication rights, please provide us the following:
1. The name of the individual responsible for coordinating the purchase of duplication rights.
2. The title of each book, activity, and/or magazine issue to be covered.
3. The number of school sites and name and address of each site for which rights are being purchased.
4. Payment (check, purchase order, credit card).

Requested duplication rights are automatically authorized with payment. The individual responsible for coordinating the purchase of duplication rights will be sent a certificate verifying the purchase.

Internet Use

AIMS materials may be made available on the Internet if all of the following stipulations are met:
1. The materials to be put online are purchased as PDF files from AIMS (i.e., no scanned copies).
2. Unlimited duplication rights are purchased for all materials to be put online for each school at which they will be used. (See above.)
3. The materials are made available via a secure, password-protected system that can only be accessed by employees at schools for which duplication rights have been purchased.

AIMS materials may not be made available on any publicly accessible Internet site.

© 2011 AIMS Education Foundation